PROPERTIES AND USES OF FERROUS AND NONFERROUS METALS

Revised and Enlarged Edition

H.C. Kazanas
University of Illinois
Champaign-Urbana

(Based on the original edition, whose authors
were Arthur Weiss and Alex Leuchtman.)

Prakken Publications, Inc.
Ann Arbor, Michigan

Revised and Enlarged Edition

© 1979 by
Prakken Publications, Inc.
P.O. Box 8623
Ann Arbor, Michigan 48107-8623

Second Printing: 1980
Third Printing: 1985
Fourth Printing: 1990
Fifth Printing: 1994
Six Printing: 1998

ISBN: 0-911168-39-7

Library of Congress Catalog Card Number: 78-70035

Printed in the United States of America

To Nury, Chris, and Luisa, whose patience and understanding have been my inspiration.

Contents

Preface

The purpose of this book is to serve as a manual for students and teachers involved in such metal trades as toolmaking, diemaking, drafting, machining, sheet metal work, and welding. The book has been designed to serve as an introductory course, with each unit comprising a lesson. It covers the composition, production, properties, and uses of ferrous and nonferrous metals and their alloys. The intent has been to present the facts, principles, and processes of the most commonly used metals in modern industry rather than to present theories. Therefore, this book can be used not only as a textbook but also as a reference book or guide in the shop to assist teachers and students. An *Instructor's Guide and Answer Book* which will be helpful to both teachers and students is also available.

The author wishes to acknowledge the work of the late Arthur Weiss and of Alex Leuchtman who were responsible for the original publication of this book. The author also wishes to acknowledge the assistance provided by Howard Sorensen in preparing the manuscript and by Dorothy Stephens in typing it.

H.C. Kazanas

Properties of Metals

Objectives

A T THE completion of this unit the reader (student) should be able to:

1. List several important properties of metals.
2. Explain the meaning and significance of the properties.
3. Relate properties to specific applications.

Introduction

In order to do their jobs efficiently, the toolmaker, diemaker, machinist, and draftsman must know the qualities and characteristics or properties of the metals which are used in industry. By the term "properties" we mean the specific characteristics which help to identify a particular metal. Among these properties are such things as weight, malleability, ductility, corrosion resistance, color, strength, and heat or electrical conductivity, to mention just a few. The particular combination of the properties a metal has helps to set it apart from other metals and makes it useful for certain applications. Some of these properties are listed in this unit and fall under broad classifications, such as mechanical, physical, chemical, electrical, and thermal properties. It is also true that many properties of a metal can be changed by cold working, heat treating, and alloying.

Classification of Properties

The general properties of metals can be classified into basic groups for purposes of study and understanding. The following seven basic groups of selected properties are common to all metals and their alloys:

1. *Physical Properties:* Dimensions, shapes, density or specific gravity, porosity, macrostructure and microstructure, weight.
2. *Chemical Properties:* Oxide or compound composition, acidity, alkalinity, resistance to corrosion or weathering.
3. *Mechanical Properties:* Strength: tension, compression, shear; flexure; static; impact and endurance; stiffness; elasticity; plasticity; ductility; brittleness.

4. *Thermal Properties:* Specific heat, expansion, conductivity.
5. *Electromagnetic Properties:* Conductivity, magnetic permeability, galvanic action.
6. *Optical Properties:* Color, light transmission, light reflection.
7. *Acoustical Properties:* Sound transmission, sound reflection.

Not all properties are of equal importance to all metals for all applications. However, there are certain ones which are important and should be remembered; they are described in the next section.

Important Properties of Metals

Strength is the ability of a metal to resist applied forces or to resist deformation. There are a number of terms related to the measurement of strength, such as tensile strength, compressive strength, fatigue strength, and shear strength. These produce what is called a stress on the metal if a load is applied.

Stress is a pressure which tends to pull a metal apart or compress, twist, or shear it, depending on the direction and nature of the applied load. A stress which causes a metal to be stretched is called *tensile stress.* A stress which causes a metal to get shorter is called *compressive stress.* A stress which causes a metal to divide into layers is called *shear stress.* Flexure or bending is an example of a combination of tensile and compressive stress. Torsion or twisting is an example of shear stress.

Strain is the percent change in length during elongation or contraction. If a wire is stretched under a load, the percent strain or the increase in length can be calculated.

Elasticity refers to the property of a metal which enables it to be bent, twisted, or distorted by a force, and then return back to its original shape or position without being permanently deformed (changed).

Hardness refers to the ability of a metal to resist penetration, indentation, or scratching.

Toughness is the ability of a metal to resist breaking, bending, stretching, cracking, or to be deformed without breaking. (Strength, ductility, brittleness, and plasticity are all factors involved in a metal's toughness.)

Brittleness refers to how easily a piece of metal cracks or breaks. It is related to hardness and is the opposite of ductility.

Plasticity refers to the ability of a metal to deform extensively without rupture. The ductility and malleability of a metal are two forms of plasticity.

Ductility refers to the ability of a metal to be drawn out, elongated, stretched, twisted, or permanently deformed from a tension force without breaking.

Malleability refers to the ability of a metal to be hammered, rolled, or bent by using compressive force without rupture, breaking, or cracking.

Weight of a metal is important to know. Water is used as a standard. The weight of a piece of metal compared to an equal volume of water is called specific density or specific gravity.

Melting point is the temperature at which a metal passes from a solid form to a liquid.

Color is the natural nonalloyed appearance of the metal.

Shrinkage refers to contraction of a metal when it solidifies. Metals differ in their shrinkage rate.

Thermal expansion refers to the increase in length when heated. All metals have different rates of thermal expansion.

Magnetic qualities of many metals vary in their susceptibility to become magnetized. Some metals are more susceptible to becoming magnetic than others. For example, carbon steels have better magnetic qualities than aluminum.

Reflectivity refers to the ability of a metal to reflect light. For example, aluminum has better reflectivity than cast iron.

Weldability refers to the ability of a metal to be fabricated satisfactorily by one of the welding processes, such as arc welding or gas welding.

Fluidity is the property which enables a metal to liquify easily and to join with other metals while in the liquid state.

Corrosion resistance refers to the ability of a metal to resist rusting due to chemical, weather, or other attacks.

Machinability refers to the ease with which a metal can be machined—for example, turned, planed, milled, or shaped with various cutting tools.

Activities

1. Obtain several specimens of different metals, such as carbon steel, aluminum, and copper, and experiment with them, noting their different properties as discussed in this unit.
2. Select one property and discuss the importance of that property in relation to a product or a specific application.

Review Questions

1. Is there a relationship between properties and uses of metals? Explain.
2. Why is it important to become familiar with the properties of metals?
3. Do all metals have the same general properties?
4. Why do we classify properties of metals into groups?
5. How can you change the properties of metals?

Films

Specific Properties of Stainless Steel, 40 min., color, Republic Steel Corporation, 1424 Republic Building, Cleveland, Ohio 44101.

Nonferrous Metals

Objectives

AT THE completion of this unit the reader (student) should be able to:

1. List several common nonferrous metals.
2. Describe many of the particular properties of some common nonferrous metals.
3. Describe some common applications of nonferrous metals.

Classification of Engineering Materials

Engineering materials are substances, such as stones, wood, metals, etc., which make up our physical world. Therefore, metals are part of the vast variety of substances called engineering materials, and nonferrous metals are part of that group of materials called metallic materials or metals. To better understand metals in general, the following classification system will be helpful.

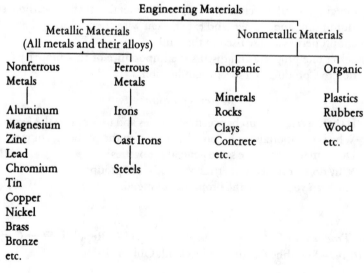

Engineering Materials

Metallic Materials
(All metals and their alloys)

Nonmetallic Materials

Nonferrous Metals	Ferrous Metals	Inorganic	Organic
		Minerals	Plastics
Aluminum	Irons	Rocks	Rubbers
Magnesium		Clays	Wood
Zinc	Cast Irons	Concrete	etc.
Lead		etc.	
Chromium	Steels		
Tin			
Copper			
Nickel			
Brass			
Bronze			
etc.			

4

Introduction to Nonferrous Metals

A nonferrous metal, as the name implies, is a metal which does not contain *iron*. The term "base metal" means a metal which is found in the earth and is not a mixture of two or more metals—i.e., a pure metal.

The properties of different nonferrous metals vary extensively. Also, any one particular nonferrous metal will vary in its properties when subjected to different conditions, such as temperature variations or heat treatment. In this unit we will discuss only the more common nonferrous metals which are used by modern industry as base metals, alloys, or alloying elements of other metals, particularly steels. These are the nonferrous metals that metal trades people, such as tool and die makers and machinists, are likely to encounter because they are the most familiar metals. Some of the most common of these nonferrous metals are *aluminum, magnesium, zinc, lead, chromium, tin, copper, nickel.* Some of the less common nonferrous metals are *antimony, beryllium, bismuth, boron, cadmium, columbium, gold, manganese, molybdenum, platinum, silver, titanium, tungsten,* and *vanadium.*

Common Nonferrous Metals

Aluminum

Symbol: Al	Weight: 0.098 lb/in³ or 168 lb/ft³
Color: Tin-white	Melting point: 1220 °F (660 °C)
Density: 2.7 g/cm³	Strength: 10,000-35,000 psi

For many years aluminum was known to have desirable properties, but until the discovery of the electrolytic process for the reduction of aluminum from its ore, it was far too expensive for industrial use. Because of its slight weight combined with a relatively high strength, especially in alloys, aluminum has become one of the important engineering materials. It is mined as bauxite and is found in Arkansas, Alabama, and Georgia. The United States supplies half of the bauxite mined in the world.

The ore is usually crushed and dried at the mine as a preliminary step in the purification process. The common process consists of digesting the bauxite with sodium hydroxide to form aluminate, from which the pure aluminum hydrate is precipitated after the impurities (which are not soluble in water) have been removed by filtering. The chemically combined water is then removed from the hydrate. Reduction to aluminum is accomplished in the electrolytic reduction cell, using cryolite as the electrolyte.

Aluminum is one of the lightest of the common metals, its weight being about one-third that of iron. It is resistant to atmospheric corrosion, is a good conductor of heat and electricity, and melts at 1220 °F (660 °C). Aluminum is ductile (the ability of a metal to be drawn or formed without breaking) and malleable (the ability of a metal to be hammered into thin sheets); it can be easily cast, extruded, forged, rolled, drawn, or machined. As is the case with most, if not all, nonferrous metals, welding is best accomplished by means of an inert gas process, such as the Heli-Arc method in which the welding area is protected by a layer of gas shielding the metal from the action of air. The reason for this is that air would permit the formation of an oxide on the metal, thus making a good, clean weld impossible. In addition, aluminum is a "hot short" metal—that is, it loses its strength at elevated temperatures. As a result of this property, care must be taken to properly support parts to be welded so they will not collapse of their own weight. At ordinary temperatures, however, its tensile strength exceeds that of all common metals except copper and iron.

Aluminum, either in its pure form or in the form of alloys or compounds, is used as an abrasive in grinding wheels, as a source of heat in the thermit welding process, and in the transmission of electrical power. It also finds use in cooking utensils, hardware, furniture, paint, automobiles, aircraft, trucks, trains, and in the construction and building industry, as well as in the packaging of food and other products.

Magnesium

Symbol: Mg	Weight: 0.063 lb/in^3 or 109 lb/ft^3
Color: Silver-white	Melting point: 1202 °F (650 °C)
(sometimes yellowish)	
Density: 1.74 g/cm^3	Strength: 22,000-40,000 psi

Magnesium occurs abundantly in nature, but never in the pure form. The chief ore from which magnesium is produced is dolomite. Sea water also contains magnesium; a large part of the metal produced in this country comes from this source. The sea water is first treated with magnesium hydrate and then processed to remove any impurities. The final step is to produce magnesium by electrolysis, an electrical process in which the metal is deposited at one of the terminals of an electrolytic reduction cell.

The outstanding property of magnesium is its light weight, about two-thirds that of aluminum. Pure magnesium has a low elastic limit; therefore, alloys of aluminum and magnesium are used when strengthening is desired. Salt water has a very corrosive effect on magnesium and its alloys. Magnesium is nonmagnetic, a good conductor of electricity, very light, ductile, and malleable. It burns with a very hot and extremely bright flame when in finely divided form. When magnesium is machined, precautions should be taken to avoid the ignition of the chips. If a fire occurs, use a foam or other suitable extinguisher to put it out; never use water, because water makes magnesium burn vigorously. Magnesium can be cast, rolled, extruded, or welded.

Magnesium, because of its incendiary nature, is useful for flares, fireworks, bombs, and in the thermit welding process, where it helps supply the heat necessary for melting the pieces to be joined. In the form of alloys, magnesium is used for aircraft and parts of automobiles and railway cars. It is also useful for lightweight castings, such as those used for portable typewriters and cameras.

Zinc

Symbol: Zn	Weight: 0.255 lb/in³ or 440 lb/ft³ (varies)
Color: Bluish-white	Melting point: 787 °F (419 °C)
Density: 7.1 g/cm³	Strength: 19,000-31,000 psi

Zinc is a bluish-white metallic element which usually occurs in a combination. The most important ore of zinc is sphalerite or zinc sulfide. Most of the zinc ore produced in the United States comes from Kansas, Missouri, and Oklahoma. Other-nation producers are Belgium, Germany, Canada, and Poland. The ores are refined by a process of roasting, reducing, and refining. The ore is heated in a furnace to transform zinc sulfide to zinc oxide. The zinc oxide is then heated with carbon, zinc being left in the free state.

Zinc is a moderately hard, somewhat brittle metal with a weight slightly less than that of iron. At temperatures of 212 °F to 302 °F it becomes malleable and ductile and can be rolled into sheets or drawn into wire, without becoming brittle again when it cools down. If, however, the zinc is heated to 572 °F and then cooled down, it once again becomes brittle.

Zinc is used principally in galvanizing iron and steel. The galvanizing is accomplished by either a dipping operation or electrolytic plating, or by sherardizing—a process whereby zinc is vaporized and then condensed on the metal to be plated. It is also used in making die-cast alloys and as an alloying element in the making of brass and nickel silver or German silver. Sheet zinc may be used for roofing or drain pipes and it serves as a container for dry cells. Zinc is used in the manufacture of bearings, castings, pipes, fences, and wire.

Lead

Symbol: Pb	Weight: 0.410 lb/in³ or 708 lb/ft³
Color: Blue-gray	Melting point: 621 °F (327 °C)
Density: 11.34 g/cm³	Strength: 2,200-5,000 psi

Lead sulfide is the most important ore of lead. Lead also occurs in other forms, such as carbonate and sulfate. Missouri, Utah, and Idaho are the leading lead ore mining states in the United States. Austria, Canada, and Mexico are the other lead-producing countries.

Lead is a soft, malleable, heavy metal. It is not ductile and has little mechanical strength. It resists atmospheric corrosion and the action of some acids. The fumes from the burning of molten lead are extremely harmful because they tend to accumulate in the body and are poisonous, resulting, over a period of time, in lead poisoning which may prove fatal.

Lead, because of its resistance to corrosion, is used for lining vats or tanks, waste pipes, cable coverings, and batteries. It also is used in making such alloys as solder, bearing metal, type metal, and terne plate. White lead and red lead are oxides of lead which are used as bases for paints. The diemaker finds lead useful when he is shearing in die sections or checking forming dies for metal thickness. Lead has excellent ductility and electrical properties, but has no cold welding properties.

Tin

Symbol: Sn   Weight: 0.263 lb/in³ or 455 lb/ft³
Color: Bright white   Melting point: 449 °F (232 °C)
Density: 7.29 g/cm³   Strength: 21,000-38,000 psi

Tin is obtained from the oxide cassiterite, which is a dark-colored mineral and the chief source of metallic tin. While tin can be found in its free state, it does not occur in this manner to any extent. Malaysia has about 35 percent of the world's deposits of tin ore. Tin ore is mined by hand labor, dredging, and gravel pumps. As the tin ore content is small, it is concentrated by screening and sluicing. Impurities such as iron ore are sometimes removed by roasting and treating the ore with hydrochloric acid.

Tin is soft and very malleable, and can be rolled into very thin sheets called tin foil. It is highly resistant to atmospheric corrosion and to the action of some acids. Tin does not readily tarnish, is ductile, and has a relatively low strength. The major use of tin is in the making of tin plate. It also is used as tin foil in the packaging of foods. Tin is used in making bronze, type metal, babbitt, solder, and fusible alloys.

Copper

Symbol: Cu   Weight: 0.321 lb/in³ or 555 lb/ft³
Color: Reddish-orange   Melting point: 1981 °F (1083 °C)
Density: 8.96 g/cm³   Strength: 32,000-57,000 psi

Copper is one of the oldest metals known to man and was used as early as 4500 B.C. It is found both in its pure state and in the form of sulfides or carbonates. Michigan was formerly the leading producer of copper but at present the states of Montana, Nevada, Utah, Arizona, and New Mexico produce over 25 percent of the world's supply. Canada, Chile, Northern Rhodesia, and Zaire (former Belgian Congo) are also large producers of this metal.

As there are several types of ores from which copper is obtained, the processes used to refine the ores are different. Since most of our copper is obtained from the sulfide ores, a brief description of that process will be given. These ores generally require a process which consists of: (1) crushing and washing the ore; (2) roasting it to convert the sulfides to oxides, (3) reducing it in a Bessemer-type converter to drive out the sulphur and other impurities, and (4) the electrolytic refining of the resultant "matte" to obtain pure copper.

Copper is a soft, ductile, malleable metal which melts at approximately

1981 °F. It can easily be rolled, drawn into wire, or hammered into thin sheets. Rolling, hammering, or drawing copper causes it to work harden and become brittle, but heating it to 900 °F to 1300 °F and quenching it softens it again. Next to silver, copper is the best conductor of heat and electricity. Copper, when exposed to moist air, forms a self-protecting film which will resist any further corrosion.

Copper is used for electrical work, plumbing, roofing, household utensils, and in the manufacture of alloys such as brass, bronze, and German silver. It is used in silver and gold jewelry and in coins (increases hardness).

Nickel
Symbol: Ni	Weight: 0.318 lb/in³ or 549 lb/ft³
Color: White	Melting point: 2647 °F (1453 °C)
Density: 8.88 g/cm³	Strength: 45,000-60,000 psi

The largest nickel ore producing area in the world is found in Ontario, Canada. More than 80 percent of the world's supply comes from Canada. Nickel is found in the form of a sulfide, mixed with sulfides of iron and copper. The extraction of nickel from the ore is a very complicated process due to its mixture with these other metals.

Nickel is a corrosion-resistant metal which is very hard and takes a high polish. When added to steel, it greatly increases the strength and toughness without decreasing ductility.

Nickel is used as a plating agent to form a protective coating for iron and brass. It is also used as a toughening agent in steel and in alloys such as Monel Metal, coin nickel, and invar.

Chromium
Symbol: Cr	Weight: 0.250 lb/in³ or 432 lb/ft³
Color: Grayish-white	Melting point: 2930 °F (1875 °C)
Density: 7.0 g/cm³	Strength: 15,000-62,000 psi

The chief ore from which chromium is obtained is chromite or chromic iron ore. Very little of this ore is found in the United States, and the ore that we do possess is low in chrome content. Most of the ore we use is imported from Southern Rhodesia, Turkey, and the U.S.S.R.

Chromium is a hard, brittle metal. It is capable of taking a high polish which it retains even though exposed to elevated temperatures or atmospheric conditions that would corrode other metals.

Chromium is used for plating purposes and as an alloying element in steel, particularly in producing stainless steels. Parts which are worn undersize may be chrome plated and then ground back to a standard size. Chrome plating is also used for decorative effects on automobiles and on other surfaces where a bright, polished, and lasting finish is desired.

Some of the less commonly used nonferrous metals are:

Cobalt
Symbol: Co   Weight: 0.314 lb/in³ or 544 lb/ft³
Color: Silver-white with
      bluish tinge   Melting point: 2723 °F (1495 °C)
Density: 8.85 g/cm³   Strength: 32,000-34,000 psi

Cobalt has good magnetic properties up to 2048 °F (1120 °C), higher than that of iron. It has good reflectivity qualities and is used as an alloying element in steels.

Gold
Symbol: Au   Weight: 0.697 lb/in³ or 1204 lb/ft³
Color: Yellow   Melting point: 1945 °F (1063 °C)
Density: 19.32 g/cm³   Strength: 15,000-19,000 psi

Gold, along with copper, is the only truly colored metal. It resists oxidation and chemical attack, has low strength but high electrical conductivity, and is used for metal plating and for ornamental purposes.

Manganese
Symbol: Mn   Weight: 0.264 lb/in³ or 456 lb/ft³
Color: White-gray   Melting point: 2273 °F (1245 °C)
Density: 7.44 g/cm³   Strength: 65,000-110,000 psi

Manganese is used extensively for making various types of alloy steels.

Molybdenum
Symbol: Mo   Weight: 0.368 lb/in³ or 636 lb/ft³
Color: Dull silver   Melting point: 4730 °F (2610 °C)
Density: 10.3 g/cm³   Strength: 26,000-34,000 psi

At one time this was available only as a powder, but now it can be cast in an arc-vacuum furnace and can be forged and rolled. It is used extensively as an alloying element in alloy steels.

Silver
Symbol: Ag   Weight: 0.378 lb/in³ or 653 lb/ft³ (varies)
Color: White   Melting point: 1761 °F (961 °C)
Density: 10.5 g/cm³   Strength: 20,000-26,000 psi

Pure silver is soft, can be highly polished, and is a very good conductor of electricity and heat. It is one of the best reflectors of light, has excellent resistance to oxidation, resisting most oxides except nitric and hydrochloride.

Titanium

Symbol: Ti	Weight: 0.162 lb/in³ or 280 lb/ft³
Color: Dark gray	Melting point: 3272 °F (1670 °C)
Density: 4.5 g/cm³	Strength: 80,000-105,000 psi

A common metal in the earth, it has high-temperature mechanical properties and resists the attacks of most acids. It is used as an alloying element in steels, especially steels required to function in high temperatures.

Tungsten

Symbol: W	Weight: 0.690 lb/in³ or 1192 lb/ft³ (varies)
Color: Steel gray	Melting point: 6170 °F (3410 °C)
Density: 19.3 g/cm³	Strength: 60,000-70,000 psi

This metal is also called wolfram. It resists most acids, and it is difficult to work the pure metal. Tungsten is extensively used as an alloying element in high-strength, high-temperature-resistant alloy steels and special steels.

Vanadium

Symbol: V	Weight: 0.202 lb/in³ or 349 lb/ft³
Color: Brilliant white	Melting point: 3400 °F (1900 °C)
Density: 6.11 g/cm³	Strength: 31,000-81,000 psi

Vanadium is attacked by oxidizing acids. In its pure state, it cannot be hot- or cold-worked, does not harden under cold work, but is easily machined. It is used as an alloying element in steels.

Activities

1. Try to identify several common nonferrous metals in your shop and (a) describe which of them have the highest melting point, (b) describe and compare some of their uses, and (c) identify them by their symbols.
2. Select one piece of carbon steel, one piece of copper, and one piece of aluminum; polish one side of each and wet it with water. Leave the pieces open to atmospheric conditions for 24 hours. Check to see which one is most resistant to atmospheric conditions and explain why.

Review Questions

1. What is meant by the term "base metal"?
2. Why is chromium used in steels?
3. How is lead used in the manufacture of tools and dies?
4. How can undersized plug gauges or other parts be restored to their original size?
5. How does the weight of magnesium compare to that of iron?

6. What is meant by the term "nonferrous metal"?
7. Why is nickel used for plating purposes?
8. What are four properties of copper?
9. What is it about nonferrous metals that makes them capable of resisting corrosion?
10. Define the words "malleable" and "ductile".
11. How can copper be annealed?
12. Why are nonferrous metals quite often welded by means of an inert gas welding process?

Films

Story of Copper, 27 min., color, United States Bureau of Mines, 4800 Forbes Street, Pittsburgh, Pennsylvania 15213.

Story of Lead, 30 min., black and white, United States Bureau of Mines, 4800 Forbes Street, Pittsburgh, Pennsylvania 15213.

Story of Nickel, 30 min., black and white, United States Bureau of Mines, 4800 Forbes Street, Pittsburgh, Pennsylvania 15213.

Aluminum: Metal of Many Faces, 20 min., color, United States Bureau of Mines, 4800 Forbes Street, Pittsburgh, Pennsylvania 15213.

Tinplate, 27 min., color, United States Bureau of Mines, 4800 Forbes Street, Pittsburgh, Pennsylvania 15213.

Extraordinary World of Zinc, 27 min., color, United States Bureau of Mines, 4800 Forbes Street, Pittsburgh, Pennsylvania 15213.

Lead from Mine to Metal, 28 min., color, United States Bureau of Mines, 4800 Forbes Street, Pittsburgh, Pennsylvania 15213.

Silver, 28 min., color, United States Bureau of Mines, 4800 Forbes Street, Pittsburgh, Pennsylvania 15213.

Nonferrous Alloys

Objectives

AT THE completion of this unit the reader (student) should be able to:

1. List several nonferrous alloys.
2. Describe some of the characteristics of nonferrous alloys.
3. Describe some of the applications of nonferrous alloys.

Introduction

An alloy is a homogeneous compound, mixture, or solution composed of two or more metals which do not separate under normal or natural conditions. Metals are alloyed to enhance their chemical, mechanical, or physical properties. The alloys used in industry today have been developed to serve very definite purposes. If the base metals known to man were versatile enough, there would be no need for alloys. However, at times, it is desired to increase such properties as hardness and strength, to enhance corrosion resistance, and to achieve greater toughness, higher tensile strength, better ductility, magnetic properties, and an array of other qualities and properties. These changes in the properties of metals can be achieved by alloying.

A variety of factors must be considered when selecting a metal and its alloys. Metal alloys have been developed for many applications. Selection may be based on the final form of the product, cost, fabricability properties, specific conditions, finish requirements, or many other factors.

Nonferrous Alloys

A nonferrous alloy is composed of two or more nonferrous metals thoroughly dissolved in each other. Not all metals will combine to form alloys. For example, if lead and aluminum are mixed when molten, the lead will settle to the bottom and the aluminum will rise to the top. Instead of an alloy we would simply have two layers of different metals, each maintaining its original properties. In the case of an alloy, the resulting properties are different from those of either of the combining metals. The melting point of the alloy is usually lower than those of the base metals used. It is usually harder or tougher or stronger than the metals of which it is made. Nonferrous alloys resist corrosion because of the protective oxide formed on them by exposure to air.

Aluminum Alloys

The properties of aluminum alloys make them the most economical metals for a variety of applications. Aluminum alloys can be purchased in casting alloys or wrought alloys. The casting alloy usually does not have the yield and tensile strength of the wrought alloy. Choice in the selection of a casting over a wrought alloy is usually based on cost; to change from one casting aluminum alloy to another often results in a savings in the manufactured product. Wrought aluminum alloys are obtainable in sheet, wire, plate, bar, strip, tubing, extrusion, and forging product forms. The cost of the product form will vary with the alloy. All aluminum alloys can be welded and have high conductivity. The special properties and good fabrication characteristics of aluminum alloys are very significant factors in their selection for use in a very wide range of aircraft applications. Automobiles, buses, tractors, trucks, furniture, buildings, bridges, cranes—all include aluminum alloys. Aluminum alloys have become an important part of our lives.

Copper Alloys

In using copper alloys, the major determining factors are electrical and thermal conductivity, corrosion resistance, color, machinability, and ductility. Copper alloys can be plated, welded, brazed, and easily finished. When it is necessary to improve some of a material's characteristics, alloying will often solve the problem.

There are a wide variety of copper alloy compositions: silver-bearing copper alloys, free-cutting copper alloys, chromium-copper alloys, cadmium-copper alloys, tellurium-nickel copper alloys, nickel-silver copper alloys, and leaded nickel-silver copper alloys, to mention just a few.

Brass

Brass is an alloy of copper and zinc. There are many different types of brass in use today, each of which has its own properties. The properties of a particular brass depend on its composition. By varying the amount of zinc used we can change its properties. The addition of other metals will also have an effect on the final brass.

Lead is added to improve machinability but it reduces strength and ductility. The addition of tin will increase the strength and hardness but lower the ductility. Manganese will increase the strength of brass without a loss of ductility. Aluminum will also increase the strength of brass, but here again there is a loss of ductility. *Machinery's Handbook* can be consulted for more detailed information on specific brasses or other nonferrous alloys.

Brass, because of its resistance to corrosion, along with good wearing qualities, finds many uses. It can be cast, rolled, forged, and easily machined. It is used for plumbing, hardware, brazing, and as a wearing surface. Wear plates and bushings are made of brass because they offer less resistance to movement and result in less scoring than does steel.

Bronze

Bronze is an alloy of copper and tin which is harder than copper or brass. As in the case of brass, there are many different types of bronzes, each varying in composition. Ampco bronze is a good example of how the properties may be changed. It is an aluminum bronze made up of copper, aluminum, and a small amount of iron. There are various grades of it, some of which are so hard that special tools must be used for machining them. Ampco bronze is used for bushings, wear plates, and forming sections on dies. Ohio knife is a special type of wear plate made of an aluminum bronze sweated to a cold-rolled base. Other bronzes have been developed for special purposes, such as for gears, bearings, and bushings where toughness and antifrictional properties are desired. Porous bronze bearings are made from powdered bronze mixed with graphite. The mixture is subjected to high pressures at elevated temperatures, and the resulting bearing is porous enough to absorb and hold oil. This makes frequent lubrication in hard-to-get-at locations unnecessary.

Babbitt

Babbitt is a soft, white alloy of tin, copper, and antimony, which melts at about 870 °F. Tin is the base metal in babbitt, but because of its high cost it is sometimes replaced almost entirely by lead. The primary use of babbitt is in bearings, where it gives good antifrictional properties. It has a very low rate of shrinkage—that is, it contracts very little when passing from a molten to a solid state, which is a definite advantage when pouring and die casting this alloy.

Nickel Alloys

Nickel alloys are sold under different names according to the alloy content, such as, Monel, Inconel, and Hastelloy. Nickel is used in many stainless steel products, and in many other alloy steels. It improves the corrosion resistance, weldability, and formability.

Tin Alloys

Tin alloys are used in such things as tin-silver solder, soft solder, tin babbitt, and pewter. Modern pewter has a composition of tin, antimony, and copper. It is lead-free and a much better alloy now than earlier. Die-casting tin alloy, called white metal, has some importance.

Zinc Alloys

Zinc alloys are low in cost as casting alloys and easy to use in die casting. Zinc die castings are used in the automotive industry in items such as carburetors and windshield wiper parts. Zinc die casting finds use in the electrical industry, in business machines, tools, and toys. Wrought zinc alloys may be obtained in strip, sheet, and foil.

Magnesium Alloys

Magnesium alloys are also used extensively for casting. Magnesium-aluminum and magnesium-aluminum-zinc are some of the common alloys. Magnesium alloys have enough hardness for all structural uses. They cannot, however, be subjected to abrasion. Today, magnesium alloys are used in large amounts and in many applications.

Low-Melting-Point Alloys

These metals are a group of alloys whose important property is a low melting point. They are composed of bismuth, lead, tin, and cadmium and are known by trade names such as Wood's metal, Rose's metal, Cerro-safe, Cerro-matrix, and Cerro-bend. Their melting points vary from 149 °F to 324 °F. Their use is limited to applications where the melting point is the most important property to be considered. Examples of these uses include plugs in automatic sprinkler systems and safety plugs in boilers. The low melting point also makes it possible to cast the metal in wood molds, thus making it useful for foundry patterns. In addition, the shape and size of cavities can be checked by filling the opening with molten metal, removing it after solidification, and inspecting it. Other uses, such as temporary fixtures to hold work for machining or inspection purposes, are left to the imagination of the journeyman.

Sintered Carbides

These are products of powder metallurgy and are a group of hard, heat-resisting compounds. They are made from tungsten, carbon, and cobalt. Powdered tungsten is mixed with carbon and then heated to form a tungsten-carbide powder. The tungsten carbide is then mixed with cobalt, which acts as a binder material for the powder. This mixture is pressed into desired shapes and, after heating, is machined to the required size. Final heat treating results in a hard, wear-resistant material. The properties of the carbide may be changed by the addition of titanium and/or tantalum. Carbides will retain their hardness even though operating at red heat, which would cause conventional tools to lose their edge. They also possess an unusual amount of wear resistance. Carbide-tipped drills, reamers, milling cutters, counterbores, and tool bits are used for machining metals where extreme abrasion is encountered, as in machining cast iron or nonferrous metals.

Cobalt-Chromium-Tungsten-Molybdenum Wear-Resistant Alloys

Excellent resistance to wear makes these alloys useful for metal-cutting applications. The ability to retain hardness even at red-heat temperatures also makes them especially useful for cutting tools. Conventional cutting tools will lose their edge at high temperatures, whereas this alloy group is actually tougher at red heat than it is when cold; as a result, higher speeds and feeds may be used when machining with stellite tools.

Precious Metals

These include silver, gold, platinum, palladium, iridium, osmium, rhodium, and ruthenium, and their alloys. The production of these alloys is under technical and legal requirements. Gold alloys used for jewelry are described in karats. The karat is the content of gold expressed in twenty-fourths. An 18-karat gold alloy would contain 18/24 gold (75 percent by weight). Other than jewelry, there are many industrial applications of precious metals.

Activities

1. Select one of the nonferrous alloys discussed in this unit and research its historical development.
2. Look around your shop or laboratory and identify as many of the non-ferrous alloys as you can; list three basic properties for each.
3. Select a project made with a nonferrous alloy and state whether or not that alloy could be substituted for another with similar properties.

Review Questions

1. Define the term "nonferrous alloy".
2. Under what conditions would you use sintered-carbide-tipped tools? Why?
3. What metals are alloyed together to make brass?
4. Is it possible to form a nonferrous alloy by combining any two nonfer-rous metals? Explain your answer.
5. Where is bronze used in tool and die work? Explain why.
6. Why must sintered-carbide-tipped tools be used and handled with care?
7. How may the properties of a brass or a bronze be changed?
8. What are the main types of alloys used in die casting?
9. Why are brasses and bronzes used as wearing surfaces for steel?
10. From your shop experiences, describe some of the possible uses of the low-melting-point alloys.
11. What advantages do nonferrous alloys have over base nonferrous metals?
12. What two metals are alloyed together to make bronze?
13. What is babbitt used for? Explain why.

14. What are sintered carbides used for?
15. How is gold measured?

Films

Copper and Its Alloys, 25 min., color, Revere Copper and Brass Company, 5801 West Jefferson Avenue, Detroit, Michigan 48209.

Superior Story, 30 min., color, Superior Steel Corporation, Carnegie, Pennsylvania 15106.

Chemistry of Aluminum, 16 min., color, Reynolds Metals Company, P.O. Box 27003, Richmond, Virginia 23261.

Production of Irons and Steels

Objectives

A T THE completion of this unit the reader (student) should be able to:

1. List the raw materials used in the production of iron.
2. Describe the functioning of the blast furnace.
3. Briefly describe the three common steelmaking processes.
4. Distinguish between the two major routes that steel takes when it arrives at the rolling mill.

Introduction

Steel can be considered the most important of all metals used in manufacturing and construction. Practically everyone uses items made of steel. Who is there who does not depend on such big things as buildings and bridges to such small items as safety pins, staples, or paper clips? Steel is a ferrous alloy; the machinist and tool and die maker have constant contact with this group of metals. This unit deals with the production of iron and its conversion into cast iron and steels.

Raw Materials

Iron Ore: The element iron is abundant in the earth. It is rarely found as a metal, except as a meteorite or in some minerals. Iron is usually found in chemical combination with oxygen, sulfur, silicon, or some other elements. This iron material is mixed with clay, sand, or rocks. To break the iron ore down or build up the iron to be of use to industry is the job of the ore-processing plants. Depending on the concentration of iron in the ore, several things may be done. If the ore is rich in iron, the larger chunks may be crushed, sized, washed, and sent directly to the blast furnace. The lower grade ore will need to go through magnetic separators, flotation cells, or other processes to grind the ore to powder and enrich it. In these processes, the iron is in unusable powder form so it must be made into small brickets or small balls and then baked (sintered) to a hard finish. From here, the ore is taken to the steel plant and converted into pig iron.

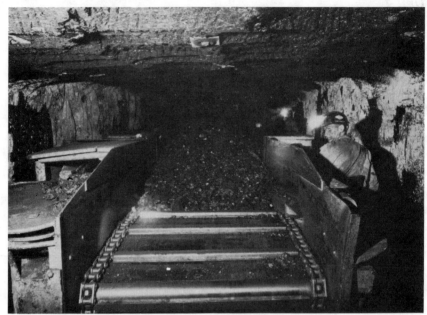

Inland Steel Co.
Coal in the form of coke is used in the production of steels.

Coal-to-Coke: Coal is indispensable to the iron and steel industry. Coal supplies more than 80 percent of the heat and energy required by this industry. Most of the coal they use is made into coke. Coal is heated in the coke oven to 2000 °F and the heat drives off the gas and tars. Coke is then used in the blast furnace to make iron.

Limestone: Limestone is known as the purifying stone. It comes from the remains of marine animals and shellfish. Limestone is processed and used at various stages of iron and steel manufacturing activities but its largest use is in the blast furnace to remove impurities from the iron ore. Additional materials used to make iron and steel ore are *scrap metal, air, oxygen, water,* and *fuels.*

The Blast Furnace

The blast furnace stands about 130 feet high. The furnace is a steel shell which is lined with heat-resistant fire brick. Once it is started, it will continue operating until the brick lining needs to be renewed or until stopped because the demand drops. Raw materials consisting of iron ore, coke, and limestone are loaded (charged) into the furnace from the top and work their way down to the bottom, becoming hotter in the process. Hot air is a necessity in the blast furnace. It comes in at the bottom of the furnace and swiftly moves up through the charge of raw material. Fanned by the air, the coke burns. Gases from the coke remove the oxygen from the iron ore and reduce the ore to iron. Limestone removes the impuritites and earthly matter and causes them to flow and form molten slag, which floats on the iron and is removed. The heavier metal settles to the bottom of the furnace and is removed every few hours. This iron is called pig iron. Temperatures reach up to 3400 °F or more at the bottom of the blast furnace. The pig iron is cast into pigs or it may be taken directly to the steel mill in melted form. Pig iron contains more than 3 percent carbon. It is this pig iron which is used for making steel or cast irons.

Cupola

In the cupola, pig iron from the blast furnace, along with scrap steel and cast iron, is combined with other elements to form cast iron. After analysis modi-

Bethlehem Steel Corp.
The temperature of the flowing iron (about 2650°F) is read with an optical pyrometer about eight times during each blast furnace cast. This procedure is rapidly being replaced by a process involving thermocouples which gives a continuous temperature reading of the molten iron.

Bethlehem Steel Corp.

Covered from head to foot with protective clothing, a workman dips a sample cup into molten pig iron three times during each blast furnace cast to obtain samples for spectrographic and chemical analysis.

fications are made, the metal is drawn off and cast into useful shapes to form either grey or white cast iron. If the metal is cast in sand molds, grey cast iron is formed, and if cast in steel molds, it becomes white cast iron, due to the faster rate of cooling. Grey cast iron has good wearing qualities but is very brittle and has an abrasive action on cutting tools used to machine it. It cannot be hammered or formed while cold because it is not malleable and cracking would result. White cast iron, in the "as cast" condition, is also very brittle—too brittle, in fact, for most commercial uses, as it will fracture very easily. When white cast iron is reheated slowly to 1700 °F and held at that temperature for several days, and then cooled slowly, it becomes malleable cast iron, sometimes referred to as malleable iron. Malleable iron is much stronger and can be hammered, rolled, and bent without breaking.

A recent, important advance in the field of cast iron has been the introduction of ductile iron, sometimes referred to as spheroidal graphite iron, or nodular iron. Ductile iron retains the properties of ordinary cast iron; it can be easily cast, has a low melting point, is easily machinable, and has good wear resistance. It also, however, exhibits properties which are usually associated with steel. Ductile iron has high strength, is ductile, tough, and can be hardened. These additional properties, which formerly were not associated with cast iron, are due to the addition of small amounts of magnesium to the cast iron. The magnesium causes the carbon of the cast iron to take on a spheroidal shape, rather than the usual weak form of graphite flakes. In addition, some forms of ductile iron are alloyed with nickel and molybdenum to obtain increased hardenability, up to Rockwell C 60, by flame hardening or induction hardening.

Basic Oxygen Steelmaking: The basic oxygen process uses molten iron and steel scrap. Therefore the basic oxygen furnace (BOF) must be near the blast furnace. The furnace is relatively simple in design. It is a pear-shaped vessel built of steel and lined with fire bricks. In this process, the furnace is first tilted and charged with scrap. Next, molten pig iron is poured in from a ladle on the top of the tilted furnace. Between 65 and 80 percent of the charge may be in the form of molten pig iron. The furnace is returned to its upright position and a water-cooled oxygen lance is lowered into the BOF. Oxygen of high purity is then blown onto the top of the metal. The oxygen will combine with carbon and other elements and impurities which are not wanted. During the oxidation process, temperatures of up to 3000 °F are developed. Lime is added as a flux and, under the intense heat, melts and mixes with the impurities and floats to the top as a layer of slag. As all of this is accomplished, the molten pig iron is converted into steel. The furnace is tilted and the molten steel pours into the waiting ladle; the desired alloys are added to the steel at this time. Up to 300 tons of steel can be produced by this method in 45 minutes. Most grades of steel can be produced by the BOF, but it is better suited for carbon steels.

Open Hearth Steelmaking: The open hearth process has such a name because the limestone, scrap steel, and molten pig iron are charged into a shallow area called the hearth, where the material is openly exposed to the sweep of the flames. A long-armed machine picks up boxes of limestone and scrap steel and inserts them through the furnace doors into the hearth. A burning flame of fuel oil or gas melts the solid scrap; as the scrap melts, molten pig iron is poured into the furnace. The open hearth furnace is considered both reverberatory and regenerative. Reverberatory is defined as having the effect of resounding, echoing, or reflection. Thus, the name is used because the metal in the furnace is partly heated by radiation from the roof. Regenerative is defined as the ability to reclaim, make over. The hot waste gases produced in the furnace are used to heat the brick-checked chamber before the gases are expelled. Later, the flow is reversed and the air needed for combustion is heated as it passes through the heated bricks. High temperatures and other reactions cause unwanted impurities and elements to combine with the limestone to form a slag. When tests show that the steel is of the right chemistry, the tap hole is opened and the steel flows into the ladle. Other additions are then made, either to the furnace or ladle, depending on the elements added. This process can produce up to 350 tons in five to eight hours and is therefore less efficient than the BOF, but it is suited for most grades of steel.

Electric Furnace Steelmaking: The electric furnace process is mostly used to produce alloy, stainless, tool, and other specialty steels. Carbon steel can also be made, but it is usually produced by BOF or open hearth methods. First, scrap steel is carefully sorted. The top of the furnace can swing to the side, thus allowing the furnace to be charged from the top. After the furnace is charged, the top is moved back into place and electrodes are lowered through the

Bethlehem Steel Corp.

A dramatic spectacle is the charging of molten iron into a basic oxygen furnace. The BOF produces high-quality steel much faster than the open hearth furnace.

Inland Steel Co.

The open hearth furnace is used to produce carbon steels.

Bethlehem Steel Corp.

This 400-ton open hearth furnace is equipped with two oxygen roof lances, each supplying 70,000 cubic feet of oxygen per hour. The water-cooled lance is lowered immediately after the hot metal addition to a position about four inches above the slag-metal interface.

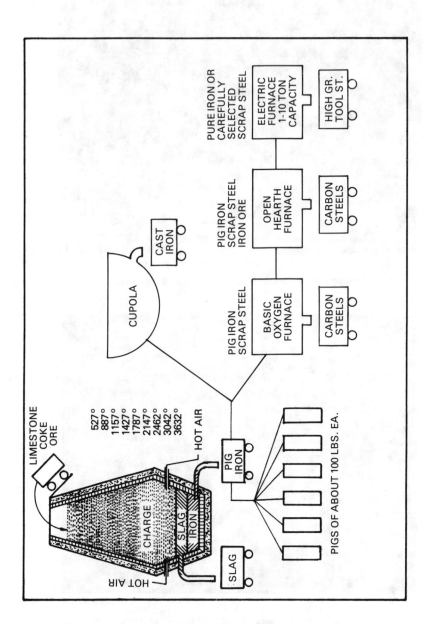

Fig. 4-1— Iron and Steel Production Processes

furnace roof. This process does not use fuel or gas to produce heat but employs electric current. The electric power is turned on and the electric current arcs from one electrode to the metal scrap in the furnace and back to the next electrode. This creates the intense heat sufficient to melt the charge. Limestone and flux are charged into the furnace on top of the molten bath. The impurities in the steel rise with the molten slag, which is floating on top of the molten steel. The slag is removed and alloying elements are added to produce the desired steel. The electric furnace may be of the arc or induction type. Most steel is produced by the arc furnace. The furnace capacity may range from two tons to 200 tons. The time required to produce a heat of steel may vary from three to six hours, depending on the size of furnace and the desired specifica-

The electric furnace is used for the production of special steels.

tions for the steel. When the chemical composition of the molten steel in the furnace reaches the desired specifications, the furnace is stopped.

Vacuum Processes of Steel

Steels for special applications are processed further to give them properties not obtained in the basic steelmaking operations which have been described. The primary purpose of the several vacuum processes is to remove unwanted gases from the molten steel and thus produce steel of higher purity. Depending on the vacuum process, the vacuum chamber is charged with an ingot, scrap, or molten steel from the ladle. The vacuum chamber is sealed, the metal heated and melted, and the unwanted gases drawn off. Through this method, the steel produced can be very accurately controlled to meet the most exacting specifications for modern industry.

Rolling Mills

Steel from the BOF, the open hearth furnace, the electric furnace, or the vacuum processes is sent to the rolling mills either in the form of ingots or in melted form for continuous casting.

American Iron and Steel Institute, 1000 16th St., N.W., Washington, DC 20036

After the molten steel solidifies, the molds are removed and the stripped ingots are sent to the rolling mills.

Ingot Molds: The traditional method of handling steel from the furnace is to pour the steel from the ladle into an ingot mold. The molten steel cools and thus solidifies from the outside toward the center. When the steel has solidified on the outside, the mold is removed, leaving the ingot. The ingot is taken to the soaking pits where it is heated to a uniform temperature. When the ingot is needed at the rolling mills, it is removed from the pit and carried to the mills. Once there, the ingots are reduced into blooms, slabs, and billets. These shapes make it easy for the finishing mills to roll sheets, bars, structural shapes, plates, pipe, rails, and wire.

Continuous Casting: This process is relatively recent and eliminates many of the steps involved in traditional operations. There is no stripping of the mold from the ingot because there is no ingot. There are no soaking pits, nor rough rolling mills to produce the blooms, slabs, and billets. In this process, molten steel from the ladle is transferred to a tundish at the top of the continuous casting machine. This tundish is a dish-shaped tub provided to receive the molten steel. From the tundish, the molten metal is released into the mold of the continuous casting machine. As the steel moves down this machine, it is

Bethlehem Steel Corp.

Perfectly formed slabs are cut to required lengths by an automatic flame torch on this continuous slab caster, which converts 300 tons of molten steel into heavy slabs in 45 minutes.

Bethlehem Steel Corp.

Steel plate is rolled through the finishing unit of this Bethlehem Steel Corporation sheared plate mill.

chilled by a water spray. The metal begins to form a skin, becoming thicker as the steel moves through the casting machine, and eventually becomes solid throughout. As the steel continues, a torch cuts off sections at the desired length. The continuous casting process is able to produce blooms, slabs, or billets. As these are cut to desired lengths, they are run directly to the finishing mills and rolled into the various shapes as described in the ingot molds process.

Activities

DIFFERENCE BETWEEN CAST IRON AND STEEL

Problem

To show one important physical characteristic difference between cast iron and steel.

Materials and Equipment

—Cast iron rod: 1/4" diameter and 4" long (use a piece of a cast iron welding rod).

—Soft steel rod: 1/4" diameter and 4" long (use a steel nail from the hardware store).

—Metal file.

—Two pliers.

—Safety glasses.

Procedure
1. File a small notch two inches from the end of both the cast iron and steel rods.
2. Using the pliers, grasp each end of the cast iron rod and bend it. What happens to the cast iron rod?
3. Do the same to the soft steel rod. What happens to the steel rod?

Results

Write up your observations of this activity and relate the results to the content of this unit.

Review Questions

1. What is the difference between cast iron and steel?
2. Why is it not common practice to produce certain steels in the electric furnace?
3. Is the basic oxygen furnace more efficient in producing carbon steels? Why?
4. Why is the continuous casting process more efficient in producing steel mill products than the ingot process?
5. Explain how steel, cast iron, and wrought iron differ from each other.
6. Explain the purpose of each of the four ingredients used in the operation of a blast furnace.
7. How does malleable cast iron differ from grey cast iron?
8. What is the difference between hot-rolled and cold-rolled steel?
9. Why must a certain amount of metal be removed from the surface of a piece of tool steel when making tools or dies which are to be hardened?
10. Describe the type of furnace used for the production of high speed steel and explain why this type of furnace is used.
11. What type of steel is obtained from the open hearth furnace? What is it used for?
12. What is done with refined steel after it is tapped from the basic oxygen, open hearth, or electric furnaces?
13. What is the basic oxygen process of making steel?
14. What is the difference between an ingot and a billet?
15. List the properties of ductile cast iron.

Films

Steel, Man's Servant, 38 min., color, Cleveland Film Distribution Center, American Steel and Wire Division, Rockefeller Building, Cleveland, Ohio 44113.

Steelmaking Today, 29 min., color, United States Bureau of Mines, 4800 Forbes Avenue, Pittsburgh, Pennsylvania 15213.

Chemistry of Iron and Steel, 14 min., color, United States Steel Corporation, 208 South LaSalle Street, Chicago, Illinois 60690.

Cast Iron—The Biography of a Metal, 27 min., color, United States Bureau of Mines, 4800 Forbes Avenue, Pittsburgh, Pennsylvania 15213.

The Magic of Sulphur, 26 min., color, United States Bureau of Mines, 4800 Forbes Avenue, Pittsburgh, Pennsylvania 15213.

The World of Phosphorus, 27 min., color, United States Bureau of Mines, 4800 Forbes Avenue, Pittsburgh, Pennsylvania 15213.

Steel by Stopwatch (BOF), 24 min., color, Jones and Laughlin Steel Corporation, 3 Gateway Center, Pittsburgh, Pennsylvania 15230.

Continuous Casting at Roblin Steel, 20 min., color, Roblin Industries, Inc., 101 East Avenue, North Tonawanda, New York 14121.

Plain Carbon
and Alloy Steels

Objectives

A T THE completion of this unit the reader (student) should be able to:

1. Distinguish between plain carbon and alloy steels.
2. Describe some of the plain carbon steels and their characteristics.
3. Describe some of the alloy steels and their characteristics.
4. List the common alloying elements used in steels and describe their effects on the properties of steels.

Introduction

There are a great variety of steels produced today. Steels can be grouped or classified on the basis of chemical composition, mechanical properties, heat treatment response, ease of machining, ability to be fabricated into specified parts, and usage. They are classified to help both the producer and user. Often the broad categories of carbon steels, alloy steels, and special steels are used.

Plain Carbon Steels

The majority of steel today is of the plain carbon type. Plain carbon steel is just what its name indicates. It is a steel that has no alloying elements in it other than carbon; rather, it consists of iron and carbon. Small amounts of other elements may be present but their percentage is so small that they are not considered as alloying elements. Phosphorus and sulfur, for example, may be present as impurities in some of the grades of plain carbon steel, while manganese in small amounts is added to all types of steel because of its ability to avoid blow holes during production. Plain carbon steels fall in the range between pure iron and cast iron. Carbon steel products from the mill cover a range of compositions, properties, and applications. The carbon content of plain carbon steel has considerable effect on the properties of the steel. To be able to better understand the effects of varying amounts of carbon, the plain carbon steels are broken down into three major classifications: (1) low carbon steel, (2) medium carbon steel, and (3) high carbon steel.

CARBON CONTENT OF CARBON STEELS FOR DIFFERENT USES

Carbon Range (Percentage)	Uses of Carbon Steel
0.02-0.12	Chain, stampings, rivets, nails, wire, pipe. Used when very soft, plastic steel is needed.
0.12-0.20	Structural steels, machine parts. A soft and tough steel. For case-hardened machine parts, screws.
0.20-0.30	Gears, shafting, bars, bases, levers, etc. A better grade of machine and structural steel.
0.30-0.40	Lead screws, gears, worms, spindles, shafts, machine parts. Responds to heat treatment, but is often used in the natural condition.
0.40-0.50	Crankshafts, gears, axles, mandrels, tool shanks, and heat-treated machine parts.
0.50-0.70	Drop hammer dies, set screws, screw drivers, arbors. A low carbon tool steel. Used where a keen edge is not necessary, but shock strength is needed.
0.70-0.80	Anvil faces, band saws, hammers, wrenches, cable wire, etc. A tough and hard steel.
0.80-0.90	Punches for metal, rock drills, shear blades, cold chisels, rivet sets, and many hand tools.
0.90-1.00	Springs, cutting tools, press tools, and striking dies. Used for hardness and high tensile strength.
1.00-1.10	Drills, taps, milling cutters, knives, etc.
1.10-1.20	Drills, taps, knives, cold cutting dies, woodworking tools.
1.20-1.30	Files, reamers, knives, tools for cutting wood and brass.
1.30-1.40	Boring and finishing tools, razors, saws, instruments and machine parts where maximum resistance to wear is needed. Use when a keen cutting edge is necessary.

Low Carbon Steels: The carbon content in these steels is between 0.10 and 0.25 percent. In terms of tons of steel produced, the low carbon steels are very significant. Because of the low carbon content, they are not hard and not used for hardening. These steels can be given conditioning treatment such as process annealing to prepare the steel for certain fabrication operations. They can be cast, case-hardened, and quenched and tempered to improve mechanical properties. However, the improvement gained by quenching and tempering is usually not worth the cost. Low carbon steels are easily welded by all of the commercial welding processes and can be easily forged. Low carbon steels with less than 0.15 percent carbon have poor machinability. These steels are used extensively as structural members in bridges, buildings, and ships.

Medium Carbon Steels: The carbon content in these steels is between 0.25 and 0.55 percent. Because of the higher carbon content, these steels usually respond to heat treatment and are used for hardening and tempering. They can be satisfactorily welded by the common welding methods, but care must be used in the selection of the welding rod. Also preheating and post-heating may be necessary. As the carbon content increases, the forgeability decreases. Medium carbon steel grades have excellent machinability. These steels seem to be the most versatile of the three groups and are used for crankshafts, couplings, hand tools, tie rods, and many machinery parts.

High Carbon Steels: The carbon content in these steels is between 0.55 and 1.70 percent. These steels can be heat-treated more readily than the other carbon steels. However, because of the higher carbon content, they are much more restrictive in their application. They are more expensive and difficult to fabricate because of the decreased machinability and poor formability and weldability. They are used in springs, hand tools, welding tools, and agricultural tillage tools.

Alloy Steels

Alloy steels are those steels which contain not only carbon—the most important alloy element—but also other alloying elements that have been added for specific purposes. The table on the next page gives a summary of the effects of selected alloying elements on steel.

The percent of content and number of alloying elements are specified within definite limits. Some of the reasons these alloying elements may be necessary are:

1. To obtain greater strength or toughness.
2. To increase the depth of hardening.
3. To obtain greater hardening accuracy or safety.
4. To secure "red hardness".
5. To lower the temperature to which the steel must be heated for hardening.
6. To increase wear resistance.
7. To improve weight-to-strength ratio.
8. To increase the uniformity of mechanical properties.
9. For resistance to corrosion.
10. For resistance to environmental conditions of high or low temperature.
11. To improve machinability.
12. To improve fatigue resistance.

These alloy steels can be classified as low alloy, medium alloy, and high alloy.

EFFECTS OF SELECTED ALLOYING ELEMENTS ON STEEL

Effects on Steel Improves:	Boron (B)	Carbon (C)	Chromium (Cr)	Cobalt (Co)	Columbium (Cb)	Copper (Cu)	Lead (Pb)	Manganese (Mn)	Molybdenum (Mo)	Nickel (Ni)	Silicon (Si)	Sulfur (S)	Titanium (Ti)	Tungsten (W)	Vanadium (V)
Abrasion resistance	X	X	X					X							
Corrosion resistance			X			X				X					
Dioxidizing capability								X			X				
Ductility										X					
Elastic limit			X					X	X						
Electrical and magnetic properties											X				
Fatigue resistance									X						X
Grain structure				X				X					X		X
Hardenability	X	X	X					X	X	X					X
Hardness	X	X	X					X							
High temperature service properties				X				X	X				X	X	
Impact strength			X												X
Machinability							X					X			
Shock resistance			X					X							X
Strength (tensile)	X	X	X		X			X	X	X			X	X	
Toughness			X					X	X	X				X	X
Wear resistance	X	X	X	X				X					X		
Workability			X					X							

Low-Alloy Steels: These steels generally have less than 4 percent alloying content. They were developed to improve the weight-to-strength ratio for movable equipment. By improving the weight-to-strength ratio, smaller-size sections using alloy steel could be made to carry the same load as the larger-size sections made from low-carbon steel. Chromium, nickel, manganese, and phosphorus are added to improve strength. Molybdenum is added to improve strength and hardenability. Copper is added to improve resistance to atmospheric corrosion. Low-alloy steels have a tensile strength of 50,000 psi. They are easily formed, welded, and machined. Products such as plates, I-beams, angle channels, and many other structural shapes are produced. These products have their major application in stationary structural members and in movable equipment.

Medium-Alloy Steels: These steels have an improved hardenability over the carbon steels. Medium-alloy steels can be made in complicated shapes. They are easily hardened with moderate heat-treating temperatures and usual procedures. They were developed for situations where carbon steels could not function effectively; such things as distortion, stress, and depth of hardening were very much a limiting factor in carbon steels. Medium-alloy steels were developed to eliminate these problems. The principal alloying elements are nickel, molybdenum, chromium, manganese, silicon, titanium, boran, cobalt, and tungsten. Depending on the percentage of elements, a variety of properties can be obtained.

High-Alloy Steels or Special Steels: These steels are stainless steels. They have chromium as the principle alloying element. Usually the chromium content is more than 1.9 percent. They are valuable in modern technology for their resistance to corrosion and high temperature. These steels are used in products such as bearings, scissors, knives, instruments, gears, shafts, and steam and gas turbines.

Tool Steels: These are a special type of steel and will be discussed in the next unit.

Alloying Elements Commonly Employed in the Steel Industry

Carbon (C)	Chromium (Cr)	Manganese (Mn)	Molybdenum (Mo)
Boron (B)	Cobalt (Co)	Phosphorus (P)	Vanadium (V)
Aluminum (Al)	Columbium (Cb)	Sulfur (S)	Titanium (Ti)
Copper (Cu)	Lead (Pb)	Nickel (Ni)	Tungsten (W)

Carbon: By definition, steel is an alloy of iron and carbon. The strength, hardness, wear resistance, and hardenability increase (to a point) as the carbon content increases.

Boron: This is a nonmetallic element. It is used to increase the depth to which steel will harden when quenched. Typical steel products are machinery parts, dredges, power shovels, buckets, and crankshafts.

Aluminum: Aluminum is a good deoxidizer of steel. It produces fine austenitic grain-size steels. It also promotes hardness of nitride steel.

Copper: Copper is used in steel to retard rusting and atmospheric corrosion. Typical applications are roofing sheets, siding sheets, and plates.

Chromium: Chromium increases depth of hardening, improves resistance to abrasion and corrosion, increases tensile strength, but decreases ductility. Typical steel applications include tools, knives, instruments, bearings, stainless steels, heat- and acid-resisting steels.

Cobalt: Cobalt is used as an alloying element in many permanent magnet steels and as an alloy for special high temperatures. It is used in steels that must be hard-surfaced. Applications include high-speed, high-temperature cutting tools as well as magnetic products.

Columbium: Columbium is used to increase strength for very high temperatures and to prevent undesirable changes in some grades of stainless steels. This alloy-type steel is used in boilers, turbines, and chemical stills.

Lead: Lead improves the machinability of steels.

Manganese: Manganese contributes to strength, hardness, and toughness. It ranks as one of the most useful alloying elements. The chemical properties of this element enable it to serve several purposes when added to steel:

1. In relatively small amounts (0.30 to 0.60 percent) manganese is present in all steels. Acting as a valuable deoxidizing agent, it removes oxygen, which makes the steel brittle and weak. This same small amount of manganese also combines with sulfur, which is regarded as an undesirable impurity in most steels, with the exception of free machining steels. In so doing, the harmful effects of sulfur are neutralized. Sulfur tends to make steel brittle and causes cracking to occur during hot rolling or forging.

2. In amounts above 0.60 percent manganese is regarded as an alloying element. When approximately 1.5 to 2.0 percent manganese is combined with a high-carbon steel, a nondeforming, deep-hardening, oil-hardening tool steel will result. The addition of other alloying elements, along with the manganese, will produce air-hardening steels.

3. In greater amounts, up to approximately 15 percent, manganese produces exceedingly hard, wear-resistant steels which cannot be cut or drilled by conventional means but must be machined with stellite, carbide-tipped tools, or other special methods. These manganese steels, because of their great resistance to abrasion, find extensive use in equipment such as rock crushers, power-shovel scoops and teeth, and grinding mills.

Phosphorus: Phosphorus is usually present in iron ores. Except for special cases, such as the free machining steels, it is an undesirable impurity in alloy steels since it may cause brittleness.

Sulfur: Sulfur is considered an undesirable element, except for purposes of machinability, when it is added to obtain a free machining steel. Sulfur decreases ductility, toughness, and impact strength.

Nickel: Nickel improves toughness at low temperatures and it increases strength and ductility. Nickel lowers the critical temperature of steel and makes it possible to harden steel by quenching in oil, thus causing less cracking, warping, and scaling of parts during heat treating. In addition, nickel also promotes deep hardening and, when used in conjunction with chromium, helps form corrosion-resistant stainless steels. Typical steel products are tools, pressure vessels, armor, stainless steels, heat- and acid-resisting steels, oil-drilling tools, gears, and ball bearings.

Molybdenum: This element improves hardening qualities and resistance to shock. It increases high-temperature tensile and creep strengths and enhances the resistance of chromium steels to many forms of corrosion. Steels alloyed with molybdenum find uses in tools, machining parts, tubing for airplane fuselages, high-temperature steam lines, and ball bearings.

Vanadium: Vanadium is used in construction steels to refine the grain size and improve the mechanical properties. It is used as an alloying element in steel because of its ability to cause a fine-grained structure. Vanadium imparts toughness to the steel and gives it the ability to take heavy shocks without breaking. In addition, it increases the ability of the steel to resist metal fatigue, even when repeated stresses are applied. Chromium is added along with vanadium to form chrome-vanadium steel, which also withstands severe shocks and strains without rupturing. This type of steel is used in high-strength pressure pipe. Steel springs containing vanadium in their analysis can be bent almost indefinitely without losing elasticity. Other items, such as gears, shafts, and forged axles which need fatigue and impact resistance, are made of vanadium steels.

Titanium: Titanium is used to prevent undesirable changes in the structure of some types of stainless steels. It also increases the strength for high-temperature service. Typical steel products include boilers and turbines.

Tungsten: Tungsten is added to increase hardness and toughness at high temperatures. It is used as an alloying element in steel because of its ability to increase wear resistance and to obtain red hardness. As a result it finds extensive use in high-speed and hot-work steels, quite often in combination with chromium and molybdenum. High-speed tools are a typical application.

S.A.E. Numbering System

A numerical index system is used to identify the composition of the steels. This makes it possible to use numerals on shop drawings and blueprints that are partially descriptive of the composition of the material covered by such numbers. The first digit indicates the predominant alloying element; the second indicates the approximate percentage of carbon (in hundredths of 1 percent) which is used in the alloy. Thus "1" indicates a carbon steel, "2" indicates a nickel steel, etc. In the case of carbon steels, the second digit is zero because there is no predominant alloying element. To distinguish the free-cutting steels from the plain carbon steels, the second digit is 1. Thus, "1020" indicates a carbon steel of approximately 0.20 percent carbon; "1115" indicates a free-cutting steel of approximately 0.15 percent carbon, and "2540" indicates a nickel steel with 5 percent nickel and 0.40 percent carbon. The next table shows the approximate composition of various steels.

BASIC NUMERALS FOR STEELS

Type of Steel	Numerals
Carbon Steels	1XXX
Plain Carbon	10 XX
Free-Cutting (Sulfur)	11 XX
Free-Cutting (Manganese)	13 XX
High Manganese	T13 XX
Nickel Steels	2XXX
0.50% Nickel	20 XX
1.50% Nickel	21 XX
3.50% Nickel	23 XX
5.00% Nickel	25 XX
Nickel-Chromium Steels	3XXX
1.25% Nickel, 0.60% Chromium	31 XX
1.75% Nickel, 1.00% Chromium	32 XX
3.50% Nickel, 1.50% Chromium	33 XX
3.00% Nickel, 0.80% Chromium	34 XX
Corrosion- and Heat-Resistant Steels	30XXX
Molybdenum Steels	4XXX
With Chromium	41 XX
With Chromium-Nickel	43 XX
With Nickel	46 XX and 48 XX
Chromium Steels	5XXX
Low Chromium	51 XX
Medium Chromium	52XXX
Corrosion- and Heat-Resistant	51XXX
Chromium-Vanadium Steels	6XXX
Tungsten Steels	7XXX and 7XXXX
Triple-Alloy Steels	8XXX
Silicon-Manganese Steels	9XXX

Activities

HEAT CONDUCTIVITY OF DIFFERENT TYPES OF STEEL

Problem

How does the heat conductivity of stainless steel compare with carbon steel?

Materials and Equipment

— 10″ strip of nonmagnetic stainless steel (can be purchased from a hardware store or metal working shop)

— 10″ strip of low carbon steel (can be purchased from a hardware store—or use a packing-box strip or metal cabinet steel).

— Ring stand.

— Cubes of wax (paraffin or wax crayons).

— Bunsen burner.

Procedure
1. In a ring stand, mount one end of the strip of stainless steel and the strip of low carbon steel.
2. Mount them horizontally in the stand and spread them in the shape of a V.
3. Place the pieces of wax on each strip at about two-inch intervals.
4. Heat the two strips with the bunsen flame.
5. What happens to the wax on each strip of steel? Is there a difference in the heat conductivity of each steel?

Results
Write up your observations of the activity and relate the results to the content of this unit.

Review Questions

1. What is the most important element found in tool steels? Explain why.
2. What is a plain carbon steel?
3. Would either machine steel or cold-rolled steel be suitable for parts of tools, dies, jigs, fixtures, etc., which are to be hardened? Explain your answer in terms of your trade.
4. How does an alloy steel differ from a plain carbon steel?
5. List four principal reasons why alloying elements are added to tool steel.
6. What are the differences between a low carbon steel, a medium carbon steel, and a high carbon steel?
7. What effect do the following alloying elements have when they are added to steel: manganese, chromium, nickel, cobalt, tungsten, and sulfur?
8. How deep does a plain carbon steel harden when quenched in water at the proper critical temperature?
9. What effect does manganese have on the penetration of hardness which can be obtained by heat treating?
10. How does high-speed steel differ from most other tool steels?
11. List four alloying elements, any one of which would tend to make a steel become an oil-hardening steel.
12. In what applications are high-alloy steels used?

Films

Special Performance, 19 min., color, Bethlehem Steel Corporation, Modern Talking Pictures Service, 1687 Elmhurst Road, Chicago, Illinois 60007.
Stainless Steel Tailored to the Job, 46 min., color, Republic Steel Corporation, 1424 Republic Building, Cleveland, Ohio 44101.
Oxygen Steel, 25 min., color, Kaiser Steel Corporation, 300 Lakeside Drive, Oakland, California 94604.

Laclede Steel Company Electric Arc Furnace, 12 min., color, Laclede Steel Company, Arcade Building, St. Louis, Missouri 63101.

Tool Steels

Objective

A T THE completion of this unit the reader (student) should be able to:

1. Describe tool steels and their purposes and significance to modern industry.
2. Explain the tool steel classification system.
3. Identify some of the types of tool steels and the basic alloying element or elements contained in them.
4. List some particular applications of the different types of tool steels.

Introduction

Tool steels are types of steels produced for use as tools to cut and shape metallic and nonmetallic materials. They are produced by the electric furnace to meet precise requirements for a specific use. Due to exacting production requirements of cleanliness, composition, and chemical and physical qualities, tool steels are the most expensive types of steels. The cost of the steel in a chisel, tool bit, milling cutter, mold, or die is a small part of the total investment of that particular product; usually the machining cost will be the greater part. It would be irresponsible to purchase inexpensive, low quality steel for a die and to spend many hundred hours machining it only to find that the tool steel has internal flaws, undesirable alloying elements, or inability to heat treat for the desired hardness. All the tool steels are hardenable and vary in percent of alloying elements.

Carbon is an alloy element in tool steels, just as it is an essential element in all steels. Other alloying elements common in tool steels are manganese, silicon, nickel, chromium, vanadium, tungsten, molybdenum, and cobalt. These elements are added in exacting proportions based on the application for which the final tool is to be used.

Classification of Tool Steels

A classification system for tool steels has been developed by the Society of Automotive Engineers (SAE) and the American Iron and Steel Institute (AISI). This system places tool steel into 13 types, as shown in the next table.

COMPARATIVE PROPERTIES OF TOOL STEEL

Groups and Types	Quenching Medium	Wear Resistance	Toughness	Depth of Hardness	Resistance to Softening at High Temperatures
T Tungsten base, high speed tool steel	Oil, air, molten salt	Very high	Low	Deep	Excellent
M Molybdenum base, high speed tool steel	Oil, air	Very high	Low	Deep	Excellent
H Chromium base, hot work tool steel	Oil, air	Fair	Good	Deep	Good
H Tungsten base, hot work tool steel	Oil, air	Good	Good	Deep	High
H Molybdenum base, hot work tool steel	Oil, air, molten salt	High	Medium	Deep	Very high
D High carbon, high chromium, cold work tool steel	Oil, air	Good	Poor	Deep	Good
A Medium alloy, air hardening, cold work tool steel	Air	Good	Fair	Deep	Fair
O Oil hardening, cold work tool steel	Oil	Good	Fair	Medium	Poor
S Shock resistant tool steel	Oil, water	Fair	Excellent	Medium	Fair
P Mold tool steel	Oil, air, water	Varies	High	Shallow	Low
L Special purpose, low alloy tool steel	Oil, water	Medium	High	Medium	Low
F Special purpose, carbon-tungsten tool steel	Brine, water	Varies	Varies	Shallow	Low
W Water hardening tool steel	Brine, water	Medium	Good	Shallow	Poor

Group T—Tungsten Base, High Speed Steels: The principal alloying elements in these grades are tungsten, chromium, vanadium, cobalt, and carbon. The tungsten base types are characterized by a very high red hardness and good wear resistance. They can be deep-hardened (to a Rockwell C 65 or over) in oil or hot or molten salt, in sections up to three inches thick. The alloy and high carbon contents produce a number of wear-resistant carbides in the microstructure. Group T15 is the most wear-resistant grade of the tungsten base group. The addition of cobalt increases the red hardness at a sacrifice of toughness. The many wear-resistant carbides in these steels make them suitable for cutting applications using delicate tools and interrupted cuts. Typical applications include tool bits, drills, taps, reamers, broaches, milling cutters, and hobs.

Group M—Molybdenum Base, High Speed Steels: The principal alloying elements are molybdenum, tungsten, chromium, vanadium, cobalt, and carbon. The molybdenum base steels are very similar in properties to the tungsten base, high speed tool steels. They are considered, however, to have a slightly greater toughness. Their biggest advantage is their lower cost. Increasing the carbon and vanadium content of these steels will increase the wear resistance, and increasing cobalt will raise the red hardness. The M group tool steels are more sensitive and more difficult to heat treat than the T group tool steels. Typical applications are cutting tools of all kinds.

Group H11-H16—Chromium Base, Hot Work Steels: The principal alloying elements are chromium and tungsten, with some molybdenum and vanadium. They have a good resistance to softening under heat because of the medium chromium content and carbide forming elements that have been added, such as molybdenum, tungsten, or vanadium. The low carbon content and somewhat low total alloy content promote toughness at the working hardness of Rockwell C 40 to 55. All types are deep hardening and can be air-hardened in sections up to 12 inches in thickness. Typical applications include hot die work of all kinds, such as extrusion dies, die-casting dies, forging dies, mandrels, and hot shears. Because of the low alloy and carbon content, these dies can be water-cooled while in service without cracking, thus increasing the life of the die. One application of H11 has found use in high-stressed structural parts, such as supersonic aircraft.

Group H20-H26—Tungsten Base, Hot Work Steels: The principal alloying elements in these grades are carbon, tungsten, and chromium, with some vanadium. The higher alloy content increases the resistance to high temperature softening as compared with the H11-H16 group, but this higher alloy content makes them more subject to brittleness at working temperatures. The tungsten base, hot work tool steels may also be water-cooled quite safely while in service. H26 is very similar to T1. Typical applications for this type are found in mandrels and extrusion dies for high temperature extrusion of brass, nickel alloys, and steel, and for hot forging dies.

Group H41-H43—Molybdenum Base, Hot Work Steels: The principal alloying elements in these grades are molybdenum, chromium, vanadium, carbon, and some tungsten. The molybdenum base, hot work tool steels are similar to the tungsten hot work steels, having the same characteristics and uses. The advantage which they have over the latter is that of cost. These steels are more resistant to heat checking than the tungsten base, hot work steel group. High molybdenum tool steels, however, require greater care in their heat treatment.

Group D—High Carbon, High Chromium, Cold Work Steels: The principal alloying elements in these grades are chromium and carbon, but they may contain tungsten, molybdenum, cobalt, and vanadium. This group of steels is highly wear resistant and has deep hardening ability because of the high carbon and chromium content. With a careful balance of the principal alloying elements and because of the air hardening properties, these steels have a very low dimensional change in hardening. Because of their medium resistance to heat softening, they must be confined to applications below 900 °F. Typical applications for this group are long-run blanking and forming dies, thread-rolling dies, brick molds, gauges, and abrasion-resistant liners. Because of their brittleness they are unsuitable for use as cutting tools.

Group A—Medium Alloy, Air Hardening, Cold Work Steels: The principal alloying elements in these grades are manganese, chromium, molybdenum, and vanadium. The function of the alloy additions is to promote deep hardening and to bring about air hardening characteristics with low distortion. The high carbon content aids in high wear resistance for most types within this group. They have a low dimensional change from hardening. Typical applications for this group are intricate die shapes, thread-rolling dies, and slitters.

Group O—Oil Hardening, Cold Work Steels: The principal alloying elements in these grades are tungsten, manganese, chromium, and very small amounts of molybdenum. In this group of tool steels, alloys increase the hardenability; they also permit oil quenching with much less distortion and much less cracking hazard than with the group W, water hardening steels. The O group steels are somewhat inexpensive and, because of their high carbon content, have good wear resistance for short-run applications at close to room temperature. A high silicon of 0.06 percent steel functions to induce graphitization, thereby improving machinability when this type is annealed; wear resistance is improved in the hardened condition. Typical applications for this group are short-run, cold forming dies, blanking dies, gauges, and cutting tools where there are no high temperatures produced.

Group S—Shock-Resistant Steels: The principal alloying elements in these grades are silicon, chromium, and tungsten, with molybdenum or nickel sometimes added. The silicon and nickel increase the hardenability of this group. Chromium improves the hardenability and provides for some heat resistance. Molybdenum also aids in increasing hardenability. With a carbon content at 0.50 percent, these steels have a very high strength and some wear resistance. Typical applications for this group are chisels, rivet sets, hammers, and repetitive high-impact loading tools.

Group P—Low Carbon Mold Steels: The principal alloying elements in these grades are chromium and nickel, with some vanadium, molybdenum, and aluminum. Most of these steels are of an alloy carburizing steel produced to a tool steel quality. They have low hardness in an annealed state and a resistance to work hardening. These factors make this group suitable for hubbing operations. After the impression is formed or cut in the mold steel, it is carburized for wear resistance and then hardened. The P group steels have a poor red hardness and must be used for low temperature work. Typical applications for this group are low temperature die-casting dies and molds for injection or compression molding of plastics.

Group L—Low Alloy, Special-Purpose Steels: The principal alloying elements in these grades are chromium and manganese, with some vanadium, molybdenum, and nickel. This group is somewhat similar to group W of carbon tool steels. The L group has a high chromium content to promote wear resistance through the formation of hard iron-chromium carbides; it has molybdenum and manganese to increase hardenability. To refine the grain structure, vanadium is added. These steels are oil-hardened and do have some dimensional change. They can be hardened at 1500°F to 1600°F, which simplifies the hardening problems. Typical applications for this group are bearings, rollers, clutch plates, high-wear springs, feed fingers, and chuck parts, all of which require high wear resistance and good toughness.

Group F—Carbon-Tungsten Steels: The principal alloying elements in these grades are tungsten, with some chromium. This group consists of shallow hardening, water quenching steels with a very high carbon and tungsten content, which aids in wear resistance. Type F3 has the greatest hardenability and, because of its chromium content, may be oil-hardened with little distortion. Their wear resistance can be as much as four to ten times that of group W plain carbon steels. They are low in red hardness and are brittle, so they should be used for high wear, low temperature, and low shock applications. Typical applications are paper-cutting knives, wire-drawing dies, plug gauges, forming tools, and brass-cutting tools.

Group W—Water Hardening Steels: The principal alloying element in these grades is carbon, with small amounts of chromium and vanadium. Chromium is added to increase hardenability and wear resistance. Vanadium is added to refine the grain for toughness. This group is shallow hardening and, when heat-treated in sections over one-half inch in diameter, will possess a very hard case with a strong, tough core. They have a low resistance to heat softening. Typical applications are for cold heading, striking, coining, embossing, woodworking tools, hand metal-cutting tools, taps, reamers, and cutlery.

Activities

1. Select one of the tool steels and write a research report.
2. Visit a manufacturing plant and observe how some of the tool steels are utilized in the production line.

Review Questions

1. Define the term "tool steel".
2. List four things that are essential in the making of a good tool.
3. Give four reasons why a tool might be made from some steel other than water hardening tool steel.
4. Explain the meanings of the following terms: (a) hardening accuracy, (b) hardening safety, and (c) hardening penetration.
5. What steel gives maximum hardening accuracy, safety, and penetration?
6. Explain the differences between oil hardening and air hardening steel.
7. What type of tool steel would you select for a progressive die?
8. What quality does high speed steel have that other tool steels do not?
9. Why does the use of an air hardening steel decrease the danger of warping or cracking?
10. When insufficient metal is removed from the surface of a piece of tool steel, how does this affect the surface hardness of the finished piece after it has been properly hardened?

Films

Teamwork, The Tool Steel Story, 30 min., color, Bethlehem Steel Corporation, Modern Talking Pictures Service, 1687 Elmhurst Road, Chicago, Illinois 60007.

Tool Steel Today, 12 min., color, Bethlehem Steel Corporation, Modern Talking Pictures Service, 1687 Elmhurst Road, Chicago, Illinois 60007.

The Iron-Carbon Diagram

Objectives

A T THE completion of this unit the reader (student) should be able to:

1. Explain what is meant by critical points of water and iron.
2. Explain the iron-carbon diagram.
3. Relate the iron-carbon diagram to the properties of steel.
4. Describe the relationship of carbon content, temperature, and time in the heat treating of carbon steels.

Introduction

The physical properties of steel may be greatly changed or altered by heating or cooling the metal in a solid state. The purpose of heat treating is to enhance certain desired properties in steel by a controlled method of heating and quenching steel. The important variables that influence any heat treating operation are: (1) carbon content, (2) temperature, and (3) time. The relationships of these factors are best shown on the iron-carbon diagram (Fig. 7-3), which is discussed in this unit.

Critical Points

The term "critical point" is a name for a particular temperature. At this or any critical temperature, steel will undergo a molecular change altering the metal structure and physical characteristics. In short, steel may be heated to or slightly above a critical point, thus changing the structure, and quenched (cooled) rapidly to trap and retain as much of this structure as possible. This new structure will now possess different physical characteristics than before heating and quenching. The process of heating above the critical hardening temperature and then rapidly quenching is known as hardening. Annealing (making soft) is accomplished in much the same manner. The difference exists in the rate of quenching—in annealing, the steel is cooled slowly.

Critical points may be better understood if we first consider the critical points of water. We will begin with steam at a temperature above 212 °F, then gradually cool it down and observe the changes which take place as the temperature is lowered. Referring to Fig. 7-1, it can be observed that water has critical points. At temperatures of 32 °F and 212 °F, certain changes take place. The water at these temperatures is still water, but we call it ice (or steam) because the properties are different from those of water. Steam will scald and burn while ice will freeze, yet both are still forms of water but with widely varying effects.

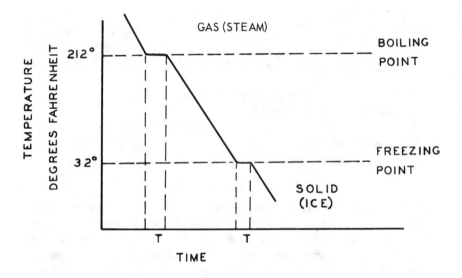

Fig. 7-1—Cooling Curve for Water

It will be observed from the graph that a certain amount of time is necessary for the steam to change to water or for the water to change to ice. While the change is taking place, the temperature remains constant until a complete transformation has occurred and the temperature begins to drop once again.

Iron and steel behave in much the same manner as does water. At different temperatures, certain changes take place in the iron or steel, resulting in changes in properties. It is these property changes at different temperatures that make it possible for us to harden or soften steel. A study of the critical cooling curve for pure iron will help acquaint us with the various forms of iron.

Crystal Patterns of Iron

Alloys of iron and carbon are used to make steels and cast irons. We indicated, in the introduction to this unit, a significant fact about the alloy called *steel*—namely, that the properties of this alloy can be varied by controlled heating and cooling.

Iron is allotropic, meaning that it can exist in more than one type of lattice structure, depending on temperature. The lattice structure or space lattice of a metal is the orderly geometrical arrangement of the atoms in a crystal. During solidification, the atoms in the liquid metal arrange or group into an orderly pattern. Most of the metals form two patterns or two types of crystal systems classified as (1) cubic or (2) hexagonal. The atoms in the metal element *iron* form the cubic crystal pattern. The cubic system may be either the face-centered cubic (F.C.C.) or the body-centered cubic (B.C.C.) crystal type. In iron, both the F.C.C. and the B.C.C. are formed; the type of crystal pattern depends on the temperature of the metal. The cooling curve for iron is shown in Fig. 7-2. The curve shows the temperature at which notable structural changes occur.

Critical Temperature Points of Iron

Pure iron can exist at four different critical points:

1. *Liquid Iron:* Above 2795 °F, iron is liquid and has no lattice. In the molten state, the atoms do not have a fixed arrangement but are in motion.

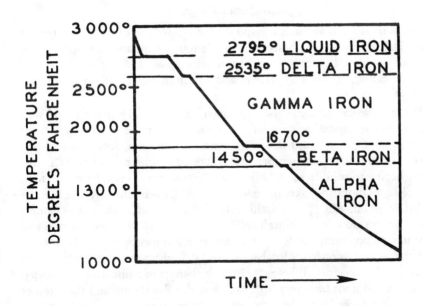

Fig. 7-2—Cooling Curve for Pure Iron

2. *Delta Iron:* As the temperature of iron drops to 2795 °F and below, the molten iron begins to solidify and the atoms begin to arrange into the orderly crystal pattern of the body-centered cubic (B.C.C.) space lattice.
3. *Gamma Iron:* At 2535 °F the atoms rearrange into the face-centered cubic (F.C.C.) space lattice.
4. *Alpha Iron:* At 1670 °F the atoms rearrange into the body-centered cubic (B.C.C.) lattice and the iron is nonmagnetic. Below 1420 °F, the lattice structure of iron remains B.C.C. but becomes magnetic. Therefore, iron at room temperature is in the B.C.C. structure and is magnetic.

The terms alpha, beta, gamma, and delta iron should be no more confusing than are the words water, steam, and ice. They are merely names for different forms of iron, each of which has its own properties just as do water, ice, and steam. The type of iron with which we are primarily concerned is gamma iron, as it is this form of iron which has the ability to dissolve carbon. The other forms have very little ability to dissolve carbon, just as cold water will not dissolve much sugar. If the carbon in the iron is not dissolved, it does not combine with the iron and thus cannot perform its intended purpose—that of making the steel hard. The iron-carbon diagram indicates the proper critical temperatures to use for *plain carbon steels* of varying carbon contents.

Iron-Carbon Diagram

The iron-carbon diagram is a graph showing the effects of carbon content on steel. This diagram is the basis on which ferrous metals are classified as iron, steel, or cast iron. Iron contains no appreciable amount of carbon, while steel contains carbon up to 1.7 percent and cast iron has a carbon content in excess of 1.7 percent.

Above line ACD on the iron-carbon diagram, the metal is in the liquid state and has lost its crystalline structure. The particular temperature at which the metal passes from a liquid to a solid state, or vice versa, will vary with the carbon content. When the temperature is allowed to drop below line ACD, the metal begins to solidify to delta iron and it assumes a crystalline structure. Complete solidification takes place when line AECF is reached. As the metal is cooled below line AECF, its crystalline shape changes and it is known as gamma iron. Gamma iron, even though solid, has the ability to absorb carbon and form iron-carbon compounds which give steel its hardness.

If the metal is slowly cooled below line GSE, the gamma iron changes to alpha iron (nonmagnetic); below 1420 °F, it changes to alpha iron (magnetic). These last two irons have very little ability to dissolve carbon and thus iron of this type is soft. For some heat treating purposes, then, steel must be heated above line GSE in order for the desired changes to take place. For other purposes, lower temperatures are used.

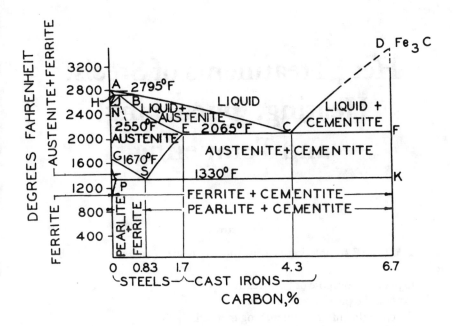

Fig. 7-3—Iron-Carbon Diagram

Activities

1. Write an explanation of what the iron-carbon diagram means to you.

Review Questions

1. Define the term "critical point".
2. List the critical points of water and describe the changes that take place at these points.
3. At what temperature does iron lose the ability to be magnetized?
4. What are the variables that influence any heat-treat operation?
5. Why is gamma iron considered to be the most important of the four different kinds of iron?
6. What is the iron-carbon diagram?
7. What is the difference between iron, steel, and cast iron?
8. What would be the approximate melting point of a cast iron containing 4.3 percent carbon?
9. At approximately what temperature would a 1083 steel start to melt? At what temperature would it become completely molten?

Unit 8

Heat Treatments of Steels: Heating, Quenching, and Tempering

Objectives

$\mathbf{A}$T THE completion of this unit the reader (student) should be able to:

1. Explain the purpose of heat treatments.
2. Explain the purpose of quenching.
3. Describe the different quenching methods.
4. Explain the purpose of tempering.
5. Explain the effects of heat treatment on high carbon wire as described in the activity of this unit.

Introduction

Heat treatment is any one of a number of controlled heating and cooling operations used to bring about a desired change in the physical properties of a metal. Its purpose is to improve the structural and physical properties for some particular use or for future work of the metal. By subjecting a metal to a particular heat treatment we can remove the stresses caused by welding, casting, of heavy machining; we can make it easier to machine by making it softer, we can make it easier to draw or form, or we can increase the hardness so that it will have wear resistance.

Heating

Heat treating or hardening is a process which involves heating the steel to a temperature above its critical point and then rapidly cooling it. The critical point is the temperature where carbon, the chief hardening agent, changes the steel's structure. At this point, although heat is still applied, the temperature of the steel does not increase; the additional heat is absorbed by the changes taking place in the grain structure. When the temperature of the steel is about 30 degrees above the critical point, the steel is in a hard condition and would remain so if the grain structure did not change as the steel cools. As

54

the steel cools to its lower critical point, a definite pause in the cooling is noticed and the temperature may even increase. This is caused by the grain structure reverting to its soft state and giving off heat. When the steel is cooled rapidly by quenching, it does not pass through the critical point and it remains hard.

If a piece of tool steel is to be hardened properly, there are four important steps through which it must pass. First, it must be heated above its critical point; next it must be held at this temperature until it is uniformly heated; it then must be quenched in the proper medium; and, finally, it must be properly tempered.

The proper critical temperature to use for a particular steel will vary and is dependent on the amount of carbon present in the steel. It must be kept in mind that in the case of plain carbon steels or alloy steels the critical temperature is affected by the types and amounts of alloying elements present in the steel. In the case of plain carbon steels, the temperature to be used may be obtained by referring to the partial iron-carbon diagram in Fig. 8-1.

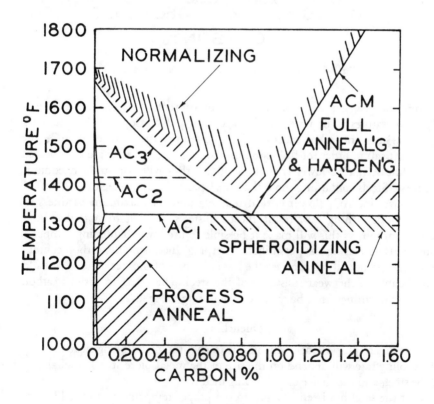

Fig. 8-1—Partial Iron-Carbon Diagram

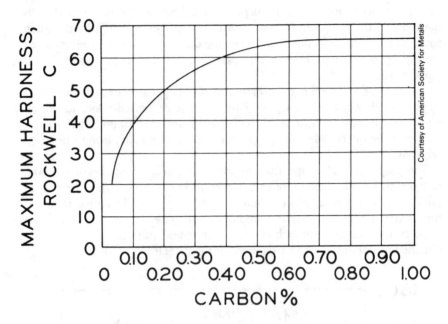

Fig. 8-2—Effect of Carbon on Obtainable Hardness

From the diagram, note that as the carbon content is increased, the hardening temperatures to be used are correspondingly decreased. Steels containing up to 0.83 percent carbon must be heated to temperatures above line AC_3 (the upper critical) in order for full hardening to take place. It they are only heated above line AC_1 (the lower critical—1330 °F), they will not attain maximum hardness. Steels containing more than 0.83 percent carbon need to be heated only above line AC_1 (lower critical temperature) for maximum hardness to occur with quenching. As a result, most tool steels will contain more than 0.83 percent carbon, as this will make it possible to use lower hardening temperatures, thus decreasing the possibility of warping. Increasing the carbon content above this point will not increase the final hardness of the steel, but it will add considerably to the wear resistance of the steel. The effect of various carbon contents on hardness may be realized by referring to Fig. 8-2.

Quenching

The primary purpose of quenching is to cool the metal being heat-treated. The cooling rate will depend on the size of the metal piece, the hardenability of the steel, and the choice of quenching medium.

After the steel has been brought to the proper temperature and held there for a period of time to insure a uniform temperature throughout the piece,

American Iron and Steel Institute, 1000 16th St., N.W., Washington, DC 20036

An operator carefully regulates the furnace entry of hot strips in the process of slab heating.

it must be quenched. The speed with which the metal must be cooled (critical quenching speed) will vary with the analysis. Some steels must be cooled very rapidly in order for complete hardening to take place, while other steels may be cooled at a much slower rate and still attain maximum hardness. This variation in the cooling rates is what makes some steels water hardening, others oil hardening, and still others air hardening. If the rate of cooling a particular steel is too slow—for example, quenching a water hardening steel in oil—maximum hardness will not result. If, on the other hand, the rate of cooling is too rapid —for example, quenching an oil hardening steel in water—the steel will crack. Each steel, then, should be quenched in the proper medium. Brine, which is a mixture of salt and water, will cool the fastest, followed in order by water, oil, and air. The technique employed in the quenching operation is also of importance. The steel must be quenched in such a manner that all of the surface area is cooled at a uniform rate, to insure a minimum amount of stresses and strains being set up in the metal. Stresses and strains in the quenching operation cause warping and cracking and thus must be avoided. To insure the more uniform rate of cooling, sharp corners must be avoided; holes and thin projections are covered with clay. The item being hardened is subjected to an agitating motion in the quenching operation so that the steel doesn't remain in one particular area of the bath for too long a period of time. The agitation serves to keep the quenching medium at a more uniform temperature and also helps to avoid the formation of air pockets on the steel, which would result in soft spots.

Regardless of the caution employed in the quenching operation, some stresses and strains will result due to the rapid cooling of the metal; these must be relieved by the operation of tempering.

Quenching Media

One of the decisions that must be made in quenching is the selection of the appropriate quenching medium. The most commonly used media are water, oil, and air.

Quenching Baths for Hardening

Steel may be quenched in the following baths for the purpose of hardening:

1. Hot or molten salt bath.
2. Air blast.
3. Emulsion of 10 percent oil in water.
4. Water at 122 °F.
5. Oil.
6. Water at 65 °F.
7. Brine—aqueous solution of 5 percent NaCl.
8. Caustic bath—aqueous solution of 3 percent NaOH.

These baths cool at a rate which increases in the order given. Violent agitation always increases the rate of quenching of any medium.

Water is the common quenching medium used in the hardening of carbon and low alloy steels. Steels that have a rapid transformation rate from austenite, and are consequently shallow hardening, require water solution as a quenching medium. In order for the quenching rate to be great enough to uniformly harden carbon steels, the water should be kept at a temperature below 80 °F and should be continuously agitated during the quenching operation. Agitation of the cooling medium allows more uniform and faster cooling action. A 5-10 percent sodium-chloride brine solution gives a more rapid and uniform quenching than does pure water.

Oil is used as a quenching medium for hardening carbon steels of thin sections, such as knives, razor blades, or spring wire. It is also used for quenching heavy sections of alloy and tool steels. Oil is recommended as a quenching medium because its use results in less danger of cracking, less distortion, and lower quenching stresses. Various oils differ widely in quenching characteristics and should be very carefully selected. Such properties as flash point, boiling point, density, and specific heat should all be considered. Care should be used in the quenching system. The proper volume of oil, oil circulation, and temperature must be considered.

Air cooling is employed with many high alloy steels, such as high speed tool steel and air hardening die steel. Steels to be hardened in air are usually heated to a rather high austenitizing temperature, held for a short period, then removed from the heating furnace and exposed to air. The best practice is to place the tool steel on a screen so that air can freely circulate past it.

Tempering

The heat treating operation which nearly always follows quenching is tempering. Tempering decreases hardness, increases toughness, relieves internal stresses, and stabilizes the structure.

Fully quenched, hardened martensitic steel is very brittle, has high internal stress, and low toughness and ductility. In this condition, steel has few industrial applications. By tempering, the brittleness of the hardened steel can be reduced yet still maintain a degree of hardness and strength.

TEMPERING OR DRAWING CHART

Degrees Fahrenheit	*Suggested Uses for Carbon Steels*
350-400	Tools for metal cutting that must be of maximum hardness: drills, taps, paper knives, lathe tools, etc.
400-450	Tools that need hardness and more toughness: rolled thread dies, punches, and dies.
450-500	Tools where toughness is required: rock drills, hammer faces, and shear blades.
550-600	Axes, knives, iron and steel chisels, saws for wood. Also used in tools that may be sharpened and shaped by use of a file.
650-700	This temperature is usually too high for cutting tools and dies, but may be used for tempering springs.

In many cases it is desirable to retain the steel hardness already there. Tempering usually results in some lowering of the Rockwell hardness reading. The amount this reading is lowered depends on the tempering temperature used and the amount of time the steel is held at this temperature. The relationship between these variables may be observed by referring to Figs. 8-3 and 8-4.

It is apparent in Fig. 8-3 that, as the time the steel is held at the tempering temperature is increased, the final Rockwell hardness reading of the piece is decreased. The actual amount of time the steel is left in the tempering furnace

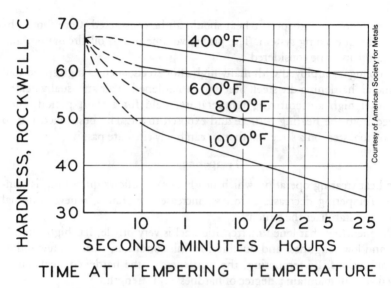

Fig. 8-3—Effect of Time and Temperature on Hardness

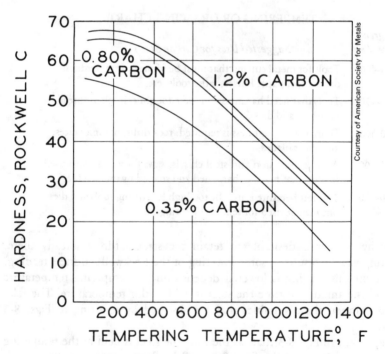

Fig. 8-4—Effect of Carbon Content and Tempering Temperature
on Hardness

American Iron and Steel Institute, 1000 16th St., N.W., Washington, DC 20036

After quenching, steel is processed through a tempering mill to relieve internal stresses and strains.

will, of course, depend on the size of the piece, but if the necessary time is exceeded too much, no useful purpose will be served. If, on the other hand, the steel is removed after too short a period of time, the stresses and strains in the metal will not be removed.

It can also be observed from Fig. 8-3 that the tempering temperature employed is of considerable importance. As the tempering temperature is increased, the Rockwell hardness reading is correspondingly decreased. In Fig. 8-4, the effect of various tempering temperatures is also illustrated. In addition to temperature effects on hardness, this graph indicates the effect of various carbon contents on hardness. As the carbon content is increased, the final obtainable hardness is also increased. Time, temperature, and carbon content, then, are of considerable importance in the tempering and hardening operations. They also have a profound effect on the annealing and normalizing of steels, which will be covered in the next unit.

Activities

EFFECTS OF HEAT TREATMENT ON HIGH-CARBON WIRE

Problem

Does the carbon content in steel affect the results of heat treatment?

Materials and Equipment

—A specimen of annealed high-carbon steel wire, or a safety pin.
—Paper clip.
—Bobby pin.
—Two pairs of pliers.
—Piece of soft windowpane glass.
—Beaker of water.
—Bunsen burner.
—Safety glasses.

Procedure

Bend a piece of annealed high-carbon steel wire in your hands. Using pliers, heat the wire to a bright red by holding it in a flame. Next, remove the wire from the flame and quench it in water. Using both pairs of pliers, attempt to bend the wire. (For safety, bend the wire away from the body.) What happens? Attempt to scratch the glass with the rough end of the wire. Is the glass marked?

Now, temper the wire by heating it to a full red in the flame, then slowly remove the wire until it is out of the heat range and allow it to cool in the air. Try to scratch the glass. What happens? Try bending the wire with your hands, or use the pliers, but do not bend the wire too sharply. Repeat the entire activity using a straightened paper clip. Compare the results obtained using the paper clip with the results obtained using high-carbon steel wire. What happens to the hardness of each specimen relative to its original state?

Test the springiness of a bobby pin by opening its points. Temper the bent section of the bobby pin and allow it to cool. Test the bobby pin again for springiness. What happens?

Results

Write up your observations of this activity and relate the results to the content of this unit.

Review Questions

1. What factors determine the proper critical temperature to be used for a particular steel?
2. List the four steps which must be taken to insure the proper hardening of a piece of finished tool steel.
3. What effect does the carbon content of a piece of tool steel have on the hardening temperatures?

4. What effect does the carbon content of steel have on the Rockwell hardness obtainable?
5. What is meant by critical quenching speed, or "gate speed"?
6. Arrange the following quenching media in the order of decreasing cooling speed: air, water, oil, brine.
7. What precautions must be observed before and during the quenching operation?
8. Why should sharp inside corners be avoided on pieces which are to be heat-treated?
9. Why are holes and thin projections covered with clay during the hardening operation?
10. What is the purpose of tempering and how is it accomplished?
11. What effect does time have on the tempering operation?
12. What effect is there on the final hardness of steel when it is tempered at progressively higher temperatures?
13. Describe the effects of an oxidizing and reducing atmosphere on steel which is being heat treated.
14. Why is some heat-treating done in a liquid bath furnace rather than in a muffle or semi-muffle furnace?
15. What disadvantages are encountered when steels are heated in a lead bath? In a salt bath?
16. How is the temperature of a heat treating furnace accurately controlled?

Films

Elements of Hardening, 15 min., black & white, University of Michigan Film Library, Ann Arbor, Michigan 48109.

Heat Treatments of Steels: Annealing and Aging

Objective

AT THE completion of this unit the reader (student) should be able to:

1. Describe the purpose of annealing.
2. List the annealing stages.
3. List five types of annealing.
4. Briefly describe each type of annealing.
5. Identify the procedures of annealing and quenching in the activity on heat treatment of medium carbon steels.

Introduction

Annealing usually refers to one of the heat treating processes designed to impart softness and ductility to hardened or cold worked steels for easier machining or further processing. It also refines the crystalline structure and relieves any internal stresses which may be present from casting, deforming, forging, machining, welding, or other changes in the physical properties of a metal. Annealing consists of three stages: (1) heating to the proper annealing temperature, (2) holding at the annealing temperature, and (3) controlled cooling from the annealing temperature. The actual changes which take place in the metal are dependent on the carbon content, the annealing temperatures used, and the rate of cooling employed. Among the most commonly used types of annealing are full annealing, process annealing, stress relief annealing, normalizing, spheroidizing, and aging.

Heat Treatments

Full annealing is by far the most familiar type of annealing and is generally done to steel which has been previously hardened. The purpose of full annealing is to produce maximum softness and grain refinement. It is accomplished by heating the steel from 25 to 50 degrees above the upper critical point, holding it at that temperature about one hour per inch of thickness, and then slowly cooling it. The particular temperature to be used will, of course, depend on the carbon content of the metal. During this heating process, precautions should be taken to control furnace atmosphere in order to avoid surface decarburization, as this will affect subsequent hardening of the piece. Any areas which are decarburized will remain soft unless sufficient metal has been machined off the decarburized areas.

The rate of cooling employed is also of great importance. Ideally, the steel should be allowed to cool down with the furnace in order to obtain maximum softness. When this is not practical, it may be removed from the furnace and packed in some material such as quick lime or ashes to retard the rate of cooling. After full annealing has been completed it should be possible to machine the steel as easily as steel which has never been hardened. Full annealing serves to improve low carbon steels for deep forming operations.

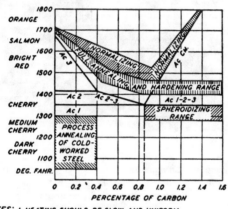

Fig. 9-1—Critical Temperature Diagram

Process annealing is normally carried out at temperatures between the recrystallization temperature and the lower critical temperature (1000 °F to 1300 °F). The intent of process annealing is to promote recrystallization, softening, and fine grains. It is also used to remove hardness that has been caused by cold working of the metal, as in deep drawn parts. The steel is given a process annealing so that cold working of the part may be continued without cracking occurring. Process annealing is often used in the sheet and wire industries to soften the alloy for further cold forming and drawing.

Stress relief annealing is an annealing process for relieving internal stresses set up in metal as a result of plastic deformation, such as forming, machining, and grinding, or from residual stresses due to the cooling of weldments, cast-

Techalloy Company, Inc.

Twenty strands of wire at a time are annealed by this gas-fired furnace (2100°F).
From the coils on the reels, the wire passes through the furnace while inside
protective tubes filled with dry hydrogen.

ings, and forgings. Because of internal stresses, castings that have been accurately
machined and assembled into a complicated machine tool may warp after
going into service; this may cause the finished machine to become inaccurate or
may prevent its proper operation and even cause it to rupture. Stress relieving
consists of heating the workpiece to the recommended temperature, holding
it for a sufficient length of time to become uniformly heated throughout,
and then cooling it in air.

Normalizing is similar to full annealing in that the workpiece is heated to a
temperature above the upper critical range and held for an adequate length of
time to allow the structure to become completely austenitized. Normalizing
differs from annealing in that the rate of cooling is accelerated by allowing the
steel to cool in air. The objective of a normalizing treatment is to secure a
controlled, definite grain size to produce a finer and stronger pearlite structure
than is obtained by full annealing; it also returns the steel to a normal
condition by removing any stresses caused by previous operations. Anything

which has been welded, forged, or cast will have stresses set up in it due to the uneven rate of cooling, which quite often follows these operations. The metal may also have a coarse-grained structure because of the high temperatures employed; unless the grain structure is refined and brought back to a normal size, the forging, casting, or weldment may fail in service. Normalizing is done by heating the steel approximately 100 degrees above the upper critical temperature and then cooling it in still air. The faster rate of cooling employed in normalizing will, of course, result in harder, stronger metal than is obtained by annealing. By referring to Fig. 8-1 of the previous unit, you can note the proper temperatures to be used when normalizing iron and plain carbon steels.

Spheroidizing annealing, sometimes referred to as strain-relieving annealing, is usually given to the higher carbon steels—those with 0.60 percent carbon or more, steels which ordinarily would be thought of as tool steels. The purpose of this treatment is to change the structure of the metal and thus improve machinability. It also serves to remove strains caused by heavy machining or other cold working processes, including deep, heavy stamp marks. These strains, if not removed, may cause the steel to crack when the additional strain of hardening is placed on it. If cracking does not occur, then warpage may occur, even though a nondeforming tool steel may have been used. For these reasons, when heavy machining is required on a part, it may be advisable to

Techalloy Company, Inc.

During spheroidize annealing, grain structure transforms from layers or plate form to ball or spheroid shapes. Here, schematic drawings illustrate the changes in the grain from the lamellar state to 100 percent spheroidized.

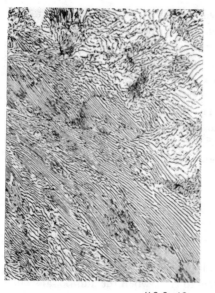 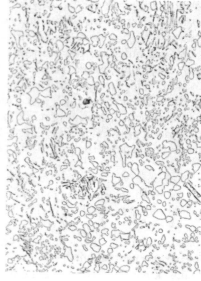

U.S. Steel Corp.   Bethlehem Steel Corp.

(Left) Pearlite as seen in a photomicrograph of 0.8 percent carbon steel.
(Right) Spheroidized iron carbides as seen in a photomicrograph of 1.22
percent carbon tool steel.

rough machine it first, giving it a strain annealing, and then to finish machining it. Spheroidizing may be obtained by one of these methods:

1. Prolonged heating at a temperature just below the lower critical temperature, followed by slow cooling and reheating operations. If the microstructure is initially coarse pearlite, the spheroidizing time may be 16
   to 72 hours or longer at 1300 °F. In order to facilitate spheroidizing,
   the initial structure should preferably be fine pearlite. Quenching the
   steel from the austenitic region often proves desirable prior to spheroidizing.
2. Alternately heating to temperatures slightly below, and then above, the
   lower critical temperature. The length of time the steel is held at each
   temperature and the number of cycles through which the steel is heated
   and cooled depends on the carbon content and initial structure of the
   steel.
3. Heating to a temperature of 1380 °F to 1480 °F. This method is generally used with tool steels. For carbon steels and many high alloy tool
   steels, this temperature is held for a specified time and then the steel is
   slowly cooled.

Aging is a natural process whereby certain changes take place in steel after it has been heat-treated. These changes occur over a period of several years and may result in a size change of several ten-thousandths of an inch. In many cases, such a small variation of size is not important. In the case of precision tools, however, any size change would be undesirable. These changes cannot be avoided, but they can be made to occur quickly, over several hours, by artificial aging.

Artificial aging consists of heating steel to the boiling point of water, cool- it down to room temperature, and then cooling it further by refrigeration. This cycle is repeated several times and results in the steel becoming stabilized. Steel products finished to exact size after artificial aging remain accurate.

Activities

EFFECTS OF HEAT TREATMENT ON A MEDIUM CARBON STEEL ROD
Problem

What is the effect of various methods of heat treatment on the physical characteristics of medium carbon steel?

Materials and Equipment
—Two specimens of medium carbon tempered steel rod about 4″ long.
—Bar stock or small screwdrivers from a hardware store.
—Anvil.
—Hammer.
—Pliers.
—Tongs.
—Beaker of water.
—Bunsen burner.
—Safety glasses.

Procedure

Place one rod on the anvil. Hold the other rod with pliers. Place one rod upon the other about an inch from the end of each and strike the top rod with a sharp, hard blow with the hammer. Observe the result on each rod.

Using tongs, heat one of the rods to a brilliant red color by holding it over a Bunsen burner for five minutes. Slowly raise the rod in the flame until it begins to cool, then let it cool in the air to room temperature. This is a form of annealing, or softening. Repeat the hammer blow described above, this time crossing the rods at their centers. Observe the effect on each rod and interpret the results in terms of hardness.

Again using tongs, heat the same rod to a brilliant red color, then quickly plunge it in a beaker of water. This is called quenching. Again place the rods together on an anvil, one on top of the other, about an inch from the unmarked ends. Repeat the hammer blow. Observe the effect on each rod and interpret the results.

Results

Write up your observations of this activity and relate the results to the content of this unit.

Review Questions

1. What are some of the reasons why annealing may be necessary?
2. What is the purpose of full annealing and how is it accomplished?
3. What is the result when steel is cooled from the full annealing temperature too quickly?
4. What effect does an increased carbon content have on the full annealing temperature?
5. Why is it important to avoid decarburization when annealing?
6. Explain when process annealing is necessary and how it differs from full annealing.
7. Explain the purpose of a spheroidizing anneal.
8. How does normalizing differ from annealing?
9. Explain why normalizing is sometimes necessary.
10. Why is steel which has been normalized usually harder than steel which has been annealed?
11. What is the purpose of artificial aging of tool steel?
12. How is artificial aging of tool steel accomplished?

Films

Elements of Tempering, Normalizing, and Annealing, 20 min., black & white, University of Michigan Film Library, Ann Arbor, Michigan 48109.

Surface Treatments of Steels: Surface Hardening

Objectives

A T THE completion of this unit the reader (student) should be able to:
1. State some of the purposes of surface hardening.
2. Name and describe the common surface-hardening technique.
3. State the relationship of time, temperature, and depth of hardening.
4. List selected applications where surface hardening is used.

Introduction

Many metal objects made from both ferrous and nonferrous metals can be subjected to some form of surface treatment. Surface treatment affects a thin layer of the outer surface of the metal.

In tool and die shops, steels are often used which cannot be classified as tool steels. Examples of these are cold rolled steel and machine steel. These steels, of course, cannot be hardened by conventional means because of their low carbon content. At times, however, one may wish to make something which will have a hard surface for increased wear resistance and yet maintain a tough, relatively soft core. Surface hardening treatment may be used to develop greater corrosion resistance, increased surface hardness and wear resistance, or for improvement of appearance and sales appeal. Surface hardening may be done on plain carbon steels, such as cold-rolled or machine steel, or it may be done to alloy steels which have been developed with this purpose in mind.

Surface Hardening

The most commonly used surface hardening processes are carburizing, pack carburizing, gas carburizing, liquid carburizing, cyaniding, nitriding, carbonitriding, chromizing, siliconizing, aluminizing, and flame hardening.

Carburizing

Carburizing is a process whereby low carbon steel, usually 0.10-0.25 percent carbon, is made to absorb carbon in its outer surface so that it may be subsequently hardened. The amount of carbon which will be absorbed by the steel is approximately 0.85-1.15 percent at the surface, with a gradual decline in carbon content as we get deeper into the steel. The depth to which the carbon will penetrate depends on the time, temperature, and carburizing compound used. Figure 10-1 indicates the relationship between time, temperature, and case depth obtainable. Maximum depth obtainable is approximately 1/8″.

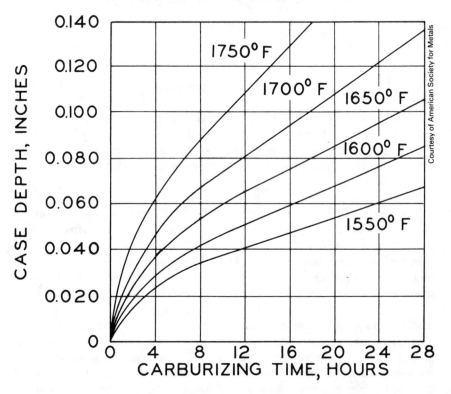

Fig. 10-1—Relationship between Time, Temperature, and Depth of Case

Carburizing of steel, in and of itself, will not cause hardening to take place. It merely makes it possible to harden by conventional means the areas which have been carburized. This fact is of great importance when, in certain cases, it is desired that some areas be left soft. If these areas are prevented from absorbing carbon they will not harden appreciably during the hardening process. This can be accomplished by coating the areas with copper or by leaving carburizing stock. Carburizing stock simply means that excess metal has been left on areas which are to remain soft. The excess metal, with the carbon it has absorbed, is then machined off after carburizing, thus exposing the low carbon steel beneath. When the piece is hardened, these areas will remain relatively soft and can be machined.

Carburizing may be accomplished in one of three ways. It may be done with a solid, a liquid, or a gas. These processes are called, respectively, pack carburizing, liquid carburizing, and gas carburizing. The particular method to be used depends on the type of job, required depth of case, number of pieces to be heat-treated, and type of heat treating equipment available. Applications for carburizing include case hardening of ball bearings, conveyor chains, cams, crankshafts, gears, firearm parts, roller bearings, and some inexpensive tools.

Pack carburizing is generally used when a case depth over 0.060″ deep is required or when it is desired to machine the pieces after carburizing. The process consists of packing the parts in a carbonaceous material in a sealed container and heating to approximately 1700 °F for a certain period of time. The amount of time the carburizing box is left in the furnace depends on the desired depth of case. Pack carburizing results in a penetration of 0.007″- 0.008″ carbon per hour. The pieces may be hardened by quenching them directly from the carburizing box or they may be allowed to cool down slowly, reheated to the proper critical temperature, and then quenched. Pack carburizing is slow and rather dirty and has been supplanted by gas and liquid carburizing.

Gas carburizing is in some respects very similar to pack carburizing. It, too, is used when case depths over 0.060″ are desired or when it is necessary to machine after carburizing. The parts to be carburized are placed in a furnace containing hydrocarbon gases, such as city gas, butane, propane, or natural gas. They are heated to temperatures of 1500 °F-1700 °F and obtain a case depth of 0.006″-0.007″ per hour. Some means of moving the parts or the gas around in the furnace is usually provided to insure uniform carburization on all surfaces. After the proper case depth has been reached, the parts may be removed for further machining operations or they may be quenched directly from the furnace and thus hardened. Continuous gas carburizing furnaces have been developed in which the carburizing, quenching, and tempering cycles are carried out in the same furnace as the work progresses on a conveyor from one operation to the next.

Liquid carburizing is generally used on small parts and on those where a case depth of 0.060″ or less is desired. It is a faster process than pack or gas carburizing and results in a case depth of 0.015″-0.020″ during the first hour, followed by a penetration of approximately 0.010″ carbon in succeeding hours. It is generally not used when it is desired to machine parts after carburizing

Bethlehem Steel Corp.

Vacuum-degassed hardened steel rolls of this type are used for cold-rolling steel
sheet, strip, tinplate, and nonferrous metals.

because the cyanide used in the bath results in some hardening taking place
during the carburizing. The process consists of immersing the parts to be carburized in a bath of cyaniding salt to which carbon energizer pellets have been
added. The temperature range of the salt bath is 1550°F-1750°F. At the
lower temperatures, the process is sometimes called cyaniding.

Cyaniding
    Cyaniding is a method whereby low carbon steels are made to absorb carbon
and nitrogen in their outer layers, usually to a depth of 0.003"-0.020". The
procedure may be carried out with a liquid or a gas. Liquid cyaniding involves

heating the parts in a bath of cyanide salt at a temperature of 1550 °F-1600 °F. They are held at this temperature from 15 minutes to two hours, depending on the desired case depth, and are then quenched in brine, water, or oil. The faster quenches will, of course, result in greater final hardness. It should be kept in mind that cyaniding salts and their fumes are deadly poisons; extreme caution should be exercised when working around them. If wet parts are thrown into a cyanide bath, considerable spattering of the cyanide may occur and serious burns on the careless or uninformed person may result. The cyaniding operation should be carried out in a well-ventilated room and the baths should be provided with vented hoods to carry off the fumes.

Nitriding

Nitriding is similar to gas carburizing but nitrogen instead of carbon is added to the surface of the steel. Nitriding is done at a rather low temperature range of 930 °F-1000 °F, which is below the lower critical temperature. The maximum hardness obtained from carburizing is Rockwell C 67, but by nitriding it is possible to obtain surface hardness values estimated to be in excess of Rockwell C 74. The surface hardness of thin, special nickel steels (called nitralloy steels) containing aluminum, chromium, molybdenum, and vanadium have been developed for use in nitriding. These steels are age-hardened at the usual nitriding temperature and consequently provide automatic hardening of the case during the nitriding operations.

Advantages of nitriding as a surface hardening are:
1. High surface hardness.
2. Very good resistance to wear and corrosion.
3. Retention of hardness at elevated temperatures.
4. Low distortion and warping of parts.
5. Better endurance limit under bending stresses.

The disadvantages of nitriding are the length of time required and the necessity of using special alloy steels. Nitriding is used for aircraft engine parts, inspection gauges, cylinder liners, and cams.

Carbonitriding

Carbonitriding is a process for case hardening steel parts in a carburizing gas atmosphere containing ammonia in controlled percentages. Penetration is quite close to that obtained in carburizing. However, carburizing costs may be as low as one-fourth that of cyaniding.

Chromizing

Chromizing involves the introduction of chromium into the surface of the metal to improve corrosion and heat resistance. The process is not restricted to ferrous metals but may be applied to nickel, cobalt, molybdenum, and tungsten. When applied to iron or steel, the surface is converted into a stainless steel case. Chromized steels are used for turbine buckets, hydraulic rams, pistons, pump shafts, and drop forging dies.

Siliconizing

Siliconizing involves the impregnation of iron or low carbon steel with silicon to form a case containing about 14 percent silicon. The work is heated at a temperature of 1700 °F-1840 °F while in contact with silicon-bearing material. When the parts have reached the proper temperature, chlorine gas is added and the silicon is diffused into the metal parts. Siliconizing has been applied to pump shafts, cylinder liners, forgings, and fasteners.

Aluminizing

Aluminizing is a process of alloying by diffusion the surface of carbon or alloy steels with aluminum. Aluminum and ammonium chloride powder are packed around the articles, which are then sealed in a container and heated from four to six hours at a temperature as high as 1700 °F. The articles are removed from the container and heated up to 50 hours at a temperature of 1500 °F-1800 °F. This is to allow the aluminum to penetrate to a depth of 0.45″. Applications include bolts for high temperature operation, tubes for superheated steam, and furnace parts.

Flame Hardening

Flame hardening differs from case hardening in that new elements are not introduced into the steel during the process. It is confined to steels that contain enough carbon for hardness to take place. In the flame hardening process the heat is applied to the surface of the workpiece by an oxyacetylene flame. Heat is applied at a high rate so that only the surface of the metal is brought to the hardening temperature. As the torch moves very slowly along or around the workpiece, water spray follows. Flame hardening is useful on large parts such as lathe beds and large gears.

Induction Hardening

Induction hardening is also confined to hardenable types of steels. It involves surrounding the steel with a coil through which a high frequency current is passed. This current heats the surface layers of the steel in only a matter of seconds; it is followed by an automatic spray of water. Since only the surface is heated, hardness will take place only at the surface. The depth of hardness is determined by the frequency of the current and the length of the heating cycle. Applications for induction hardening are gears, crankshafts, bearing surfaces, cam shafts, and firearm parts.

Activities

1. Make a chart showing the names of products that are given surface hardening treatments in your shop.

Review Questions

1. What is the prupose of case hardening steel?
2. List three ways in which carburizing may be accomplished.
3. What determines the final depth to which carbon will penetrate steel during the carburizing process?
4. How is it possible to leave certain areas soft on a piece which is to be carburized and hardened?
5. When is pack carburizing used and how is it done?
6. What is the purpose of cyanide hardening and how is it done?
7. How does the flame hardening process differ from the case hardening process?
8. Would it be advisable to grind a piece which has been cyanided? Explain your answer.
9. Describe the nitriding process and list its advantages.
10. How is carburized steel hardened?
11. How deep a case would you expect to have on a job which has been gas-carburized for 12 hours?
12. How does liquid carburizing differ from liquid cyaniding?

Films

Elements of Surface Hardening, 20 min., black & white, University of Michigan Film Library, Ann Arbor, Michigan 48109.

Surface Treatments of Steels: Surface Plating

Objectives

A T THE completion of this unit the reader (student) should be able to:
1. State the purpose of coating treatment for steels.
2. List some of the common coating treatments for steels.
3. Briefly describe the coating process from selected steels.
4. Perform the experiment on electroplating and relate the results to the content of this unit.

Introduction

Metallic coatings are applied to materials by several methods and are used to impart some particular characteristic to the material. Coatings of this type can provide for corrosion resistance, wear resistance, or can enhance the appearance of the article. The metallic coating selected may be a matter of economics, availability, or the ability to successfully apply the coating.

Surface Plating

Electroplating

Electroplating is a method of depositing a metal onto an electrically conductive surface in order to provide resistance to corrosion, to give a special appearance of color or luster, or to increase the thickness of the plated surface. Plating materials used are copper, nickel, chromium, tin, cadmium, silver, and gold. Electroplating is done by placing the part to be plated into a solution, called the electrolyte, and sending a direct current through the solution. The electrolyte contains dissolved salts of the metal to be deposited and a weak acid or base to increase the electrical conductivity of the solution. The part that is to be plated is designated the cathode and is suspended in the solution, along with a suspended slab of the metal to be deposited. When a low voltage direct current is applied, metallic ions travel to the cathode workpiece and are deposited as a metal coating.

Hot-Dipped Molten Metal Coating

Hot-dipped molten metal coatings are applied to casting, sheets, and wire to prevent corrosion. Aluminum, tin, and zinc are metals most frequently used for this process. In all of these cases, heat is required to cause some diffusion of the coating into the base metal. The surface for hot dipping must be clean.

Plating can be applied commercially to steel, copper, brass, zinc, aluminum, and to some plastics. This type of plating finds use in fabricating food and beverage containers. Hot dipping is still used for wire, some roofing materials, and gasoline tanks. Leads are used as coatings on steel sheet, wire, and fabri-

Bethlehem Steel Corp.

Steel coated with tin by the electrolytic process leaves the plating line. Looping towers at the discharge end take up slack to allow time for welding strips together prior to coating.

cated articles, such as bolts, washers, nuts, and hooks. Lead-coated sheets are easily formed by spinning and drawing because the lead serves as a friction-reducing lubricant.

Hot-dipped aluminum steel sheets are used for automobile mufflers and tailpipes.

Zinc hot-dip coatings, known as galvanized coatings, are used to protect ferrous structures and outdoor hardware against corrosion. In mild outdoor exposures, zinc affords a high degree of protection. Zinc coatings will deteriorate rapidly in sea water or with acidic conditions.

Metallizing

Metallizing is a process of spraying molten metal or ceramic powders from a nozzle onto a surface to form a coating. The sprayed metal coatings are used to produce a wear resistant or corrosion resistant surface, to build up parts that are undersize, as coatings for electrical shielding, as conductive elements on glass for radiant heaters, as soldering connections on ceramics for decorating parts, and as hardfacing.

Metallized metals have very high shear strength—up to 16,000 psi—and tensile strengths of about 3,000 psi.

Metallic Vapor Coating

Metallic vapor coating is a process whereby metal is vaporized and allowed to condense on an article under a vacuum. This method deposits a thin metallic coating on metal and on such items as fabric, glass, paper, and wax.

Oxide Coating

Oxide coatings can be produced on iron, steel, or copper. The metal is heated in an alkaline oxidizing solution at a predetermined temperature. The applications include decorative and corrosion resistant coating on metal parts such as gun parts, spark plugs, and small tools.

Chemical Conversion Coating

Chemical conversion coatings of phosphate and chromate treatments are given to steel, iron, aluminum, zinc, and magnesium alloys to convert the surface into a corrosion resistant nonreactive form. This transformation or conversion consists of a chemical modification of the metal surface so that the coating formed becomes part of the parent metal.

Zinc Phosphate Coating

Zinc phosphate coatings are used on parts such as pistons, piston rings, cam shafts, and other parts to minimize wear during their initial wearing-in period.

Chromate coatings are also used on zinc base die castings and aluminum.

They provide protection to the metals coated by excluding water and by inhibiting any corrosion which may possibly start.

Hardfacing

Hardfacing is a process by which air hardening steels such as high speed steels, natural hard alloys such as stellite, tungsten carbide, and boron carbide, and special stainless steels may be fused to metals requiring a harder and tougher wear resistant, shock resistant, and corrosion resistant surface. Hardfacing alloys may be fused to almost any metal part by an oxyacetylene torch, electric arc, or powdered metal spray. With ideal welding conditions, the bond between the hardfacing alloy used and the parent metal is strong—in most cases, stronger than the hardfacing alloy alone.

Inland Steel Company

A steel strip rises from a pot of molten zinc. The galvanized hot-dip coating gives the steel protection from outdoor exposure.

Activities

ELECTROPLATING

Problem

How to deposit a thin coating of one metal on another.

Materials and Equipment

—Small articles to be plated—steel, aluminum.

—Sheet of pure copper.

—Tank—rubber, plastic, or earthen crock (plastic dish pan or wastebasket).

—Plating compound—copper, sulfate crystals.

—Water.

—Source of low-voltage direct current (battery, direct current generator).

—Switch, ammeter, rheostat, voltmeter, and copper wire leads.

—Copper rods.

—Sulfuric acid.

—Face shield, rubber gloves.

Procedure

1. Prepare a copper sulfate solution by adding the copper sulfate crystals to water. Add to this a few drops of sulfuric acid to improve the activity. Add the acid last and pour carefully into the sulfate solution.
2. Clean the part to be plated.
3. Connect the positive (+) side of the battery to a copper rod and attach the copper sheet to this rod.
4. Connect the negative (–) side of the battery to another copper rod and attach the object to be plated to this rod.
5. The smaller the amount of current, the better will be the deposit of copper. The plating time should be about 15 minutes.
6. Wash the finished part in water.

Results

Write up your observations and relate the results to the content of this unit.

Review Questions

1. How would you define electroplating?
2. What type of current is used in electroplating?
3. How is electroplating different from hot dipping?
4. Is metallizing different from metallic coating?
5. What are some of the reasons hardfacing is used?

Films

Hot Dip Galvanizing after Fabrication, 12 min., color, American Hot Dip Galvanizers Association, Inc., 1000 Vermont Avenue, N.W., Washington, D.C. 20005.

Destructive Testing
of Metals

Objectives

A T THE completion of this unit the reader (student) should be able to:

1. Describe the purpose of testing metals.
2. Briefly define destructive testing.
3. Name and describe the common destructive testing methods.
4. Differentiate between Rockwell and Vickers hardness testing.
5. Classify some steels and irons by using the spark test.

Introduction

A knowledge of the properties of metals or alloys enables us to determine their suitability for certain uses and allows us to modify them to obtain the most desirable form. Testing methods enable us to take a sample portion of a metal and to predict with some certainty how the metal will behave in actual service. Methods which involve testing the part to the failure point, or leaving an indentation on the surface of the part being tested, are known as destructive testing. Methods not involving destruction of the specimen are known as nondestructive testing. Destructive testing will be discussed in this unit; nondestructive methods will be covered in Unit 13.

Scratch Hardness Testing

Mohs Scales

Mohs scales are used as a simple method of measuring hardness to determine whether or not one material will scratch another. The Mohs scale rates very soft talc with a hardness of 1 and diamond, which will scratch all other materials, with a hardness of 10. The material being tested is scratched with one of the samples in the Mohs scale and its hardness is determined on that basis.

File Hardness Test

File hardness testing is one of the oldest and easiest methods of determining the hardness of a metal. This method will indicate whether the material being tested is softer or harder than the file, but it will not tell us exactly how soft or hard it is. The test can still, however, be used to our advantage. With a file we can explore the insides of holes and other places where conventional hardness testing machines cannot be used. We can determine the presence of soft spots on the surface of heat-treated metals and find out how deep those soft spots are. File testing has the added advantage of needing very little in the way of time, equipment, or experience; the method can be quite useful to us.

Penetration Hardness Testing

Rockwell Hardness Testing

Rockwell hardness testing determines the relative hardness of metals by measuring the depth of impression which can be made by a penetrator under a known load. The softer metals will permit deeper impressions to be made in the metal's surface. These metals will be indicated by lower hardness numbers. Harder metals permit less of an impression to be made, resulting in higher hardness numbers. Rockwell hardness testing is achieved by using Rockwell hardness testing machines.

There are two basic types of Rockwell testing machines in use at the present time. One is the regular testing machine, which is perhaps the most familiar of the two types of machines; the other is the superficial hardness testing machine, developed primarily for testing thin metals or case-hardened surfaces.

The penetrator used for making hardness tests is either a hardened steel ball ranging in size from 1/16" to 1/2", used for testing softer metals, or a sphero-conical diamond penetrator which is used when testing hardened steel. The load which is applied to these penetrators through a series of levers may vary from 15 kilograms (approximately 33 lbs.) for superficial testing to 150 kilograms (approximately 330 lbs.) for regular testing. The load to be applied and the penetrator to be used depend, of course, on the thickness and hardness of the metal being tested. Tables which are provided with these machines may be consulted to determine the proper load and penetrator to be used for a particular job.

Brinell Hardness Testing

Brinell hardness testing operates on almost the same principle as the Rockwell. The difference between the two is that the Rockwell hardness number is determined by the depth of the impression while the Brinell hardness number is determined by the area of the impression.

The Brinell test consists of forcing a hardened ball 10 millimeters (0.3937 in.) in diameter into the surface of the metal being tested, under a load of 3,000 kilograms (approximately 6,600 lbs.). The area of this impression determines the Brinell hardness number of the metal being tested. Softer metals result in larger impressions but have lower hardness numbers.

Wilson Instruments, Inc.

The Rockwell hardness tester is used for testing metals.

Vickers Hardness Testing

The Vickers hardness testing method is similar to the Brinell method. The penetrator used in the Vickers machine is a diamond pyramid. This impression is easier to read than the impression made by the Brinell technique. The diamond point does not deform the material. In making the Vickers test, a predetermined load is applied to the specimen; after removal of the load, the ratio of the impressed load to the area of the impression gives the hardness number.

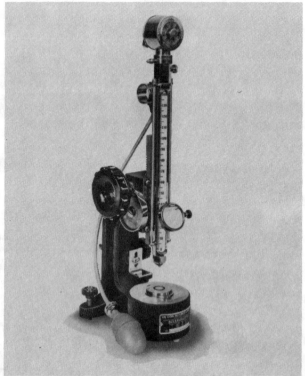

The Shore Instrument & Mfg. Company, Inc.

The Shore scleroscope can test ferrous or nonferrous metals with virtually no
limitation in size or shape.

Sonodur Ultrasonic Hardness Testing

The Sonodur ultrasonic hardness tester employs a diamond-tipped magneto-
strictine rod that is electrically excited to its resonant frequency. The resonant
frequency of the diamond-tipped rod increases with penetration and the frequency changes are displayed on the electronic readout meter in terms of hardness numbers.

Scleroscope Hardness Testing

Scleroscope hardness testing is accomplished by dropping a diamond-pointed
weight from a given height to the surface of the metal being tested. The height
of rebound of the diamond-tipped weight determines the relative hardness or
softness of the metal. Harder metals will give a higher rebound and consequently a higher hardness number. Softer metals will result in less rebound
and thus have a lower hardness number. The machines are available with direct
reading dials.

There are many factors which can influence the accuracy of indentation or penetration in hardness testing: (1) condition of the indenter, (2) condition of the anvil on which the specimen rests, (3) thickness of the specimen, (4) surface condition of the specimen, and (5) uniformity of the material being tested.

Each of the hardness testing methods discussed has its own particular way of determining a hardness number. At times it is desirable to convert a hardness number obtained with one method into the equivalent number which would be obtained with another method. For this reason hardness conversion tables have been developed. By referring to tables in the *Machinery's Handbook* or the *Handbook of the American Society for Testing and Materials,* we can convert a Brinell number to a Rockwell, or to a scleroscope or to a Vickers hardness number, or vice-versa, when it is to our advantage.

For example, Rockwell C 60, which is file hard, would correspond to a Brinell number of 654 (tungsten carbide ball), to a Vickers (diamond pyramid) number of 697, or to a scleroscope reading of 81. In this manner, hardness numbers on testing machines which are unfamiliar to the student may be translated into numbers such as the Rockwell, which may be more familiar. In addition, the tables usually relate the hardness number to the approximate strength (in psi) of the steel being tested.

Testing for Other Properties

Torsion Testing

Torsion testing is useful for testing parts such as axles, shafts, twist drills, and couplings. It has been used to test brittle materials and, at higher temperatures, as an indicator of forgeability. Torsion tests also provide a method for determining the modulus of elasticity in shear, shearing yield strength, and ultimate shearing strength. A torsion testing machine consists essentially of a twisting head in which one end of the specimen is gripped so that a twisting force is applied to the specimen. A torsion measuring head to measure the torque and a twist measuring device to measure angular displacements of points at opposite ends of the specimen are parts of the testing machine.

Fatigue Testing

Fatigue testing subjects a specimen to fluctuating loads. When a specimen is broken in a tensile testing machine, a definite stress is required to cause that fracture. However, a specimen of that same material may fail under a much smaller stress when subjected to cyclic or fluctuating loads. In this way, an axle may break after only a few months of use even though its maximum load has not increased. Such failures are known as fatigue failures. In designing parts subjected to varying stresses. the fatigue limit of a material often is much more important than its tensile strength or its yield strength. This fatigue limit is the maximum stress that a metal will withstand without failure for a specified number of stress cycles.

The fatigue testing machine consists of a drive used to apply repeated cycles of stress to the specimen, a means for measuring the maximum and minimum stresses, and a device to count the repeated cycles of stress applied.

Tensile Testing

Tensile testing is frequently used to obtain a great amount of information about the static mechanical properties of metals, such as ductility, tensile strength, proportional limit, modulus of elasticity, elastic limit, resilience, yield point, yield strength, and breaking strength.

The tensile test is performed by marking with prick punch marks the specimen gauge length and the cross-sectional area of the reduced section. The specimen is then locked in the grips of the upper and lower cross beams of the testing machine. During the test, the load is increased and both the load and elongation of the specimen are recorded. A stress-strain diagram similar to the one shown in Fig. 12-1 may be plotted from the data.

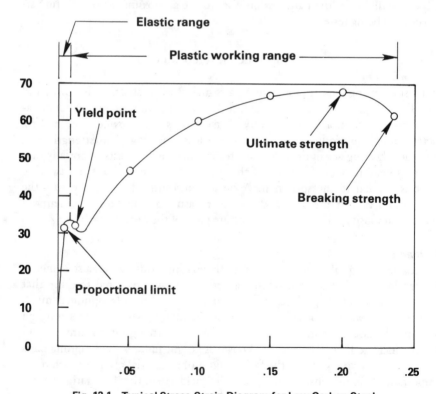

Fig. 12-1—Typical Stress-Strain Diagram for Low Carbon Steel

SATE Systems, Inc.

The Universal tensile testing machine tests tensile, compression, and flexure strength of metals.

Impact Testing

Impact tests are used to determine the performance of metals under an impact load or a shock, which is often quite different from the behavior shown under slowly applied loads. The pendulum impact testing machine is designed to measure the notch toughness of different metals. The test can be employed to determine the suitability of a material at low temperature applications by measuring the resistence of a material to the spread of a crack after it has once formed.

Two recognized tests (the Chanpy and the Izod) exist in which notched specimens are fractured by a swinging pendulum. The energy required to fracture a specimen is measured in foot-pounds and is computed from the weight of the pendulum times the difference in height of the pendulum before and after impact. A scale on the machine specifies the impact value in foot-pounds.

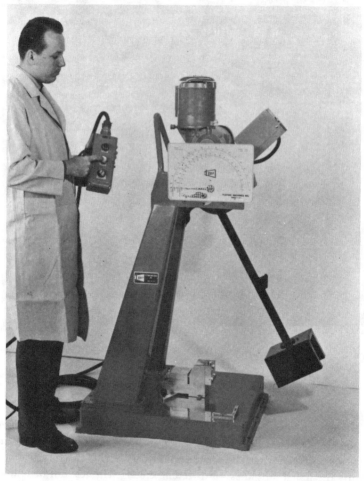

Testing Machines, Inc.

This Universal impact testing machine is used to test the impact strength of metals.

Spark Testing

Spark testing is a method of classifying steels according to their composition by the visual study of the sparks formed when the steel is held against a high speed grinding wheel. This test does not replace chemical analysis but it is a convenient and fast method of sorting mixed steels whose spark characteristics are known.

Spark testing is used to identify steels of unknown material. It may be used when steel has lost its markings, when we wish to identify usable scrap, or when the incoming steel is spark-tested to make sure that it is properly identified. Identification is based on the fact that various families of steels give off

Inland Steel Company

Spark testing is applied to these steel billets.

characteristic sparks when they are touched by a grinding wheel. The type of sparks given off are determined by the carbon content and the alloying elements used in that steel. Considerable experience is required for accurate results in spark testing.

The inexperienced spark tester has at least one point in his favor. Since each shop often carries several different brands of steel, by comparing the sparks given off by the unknown steel with the sparks given off by known steels, the tester can arrive at a fairly safe idea of the nature of the unknown steel. After considerable experience, the spark tester should be able to quite accurately identify the type of steel being tested.

Activities

SPARK TEST

Problem

How can steel and cast iron be classified by their spark pattern?

Materials and Equipment

—Grinding wheel.

—Variety of specimens, such as: wrought iron, carbon iron, white cast iron, manganese steel, tungsten-chromium steel, copper, brass, machine steel, grey cast iron, high speed steel, stainless steel, nickel, aluminum.

—Safety glasses with side shields.

Procedure

The spark test is best conducted by holding the steel stationary and touching a high speed portable grinder to the specimen with sufficient pressure to throw a horizontal spark stream about 12 inches long. Wheel pressure against the work is important because increasing the pressure will raise the temperature of the spark stream and give the appearance, to the inexperienced eye, of higher carbon content.

The spark pattern near and around the wheel and in the middle of the spark stream as well as the reaction of spark particles at the end of the spark system should be observed. A 0.15 percent carbon steel shows sparks in long streaks with a tendency to burst with a sparkler effect; a carbon tool steel shows pronounced bursting; and steel with 1.00 percent carbon will show brilliant and small explosions of sparklers. As the carbon content goes up, the intensity of the bursting increases. Other alloying elements will have some influence on the spark picture, color, and spark stream. Remember that in the experiment the operator should be protected by safety glasses with side shields. Using a variety of metals, try to identify each by the spark characteristic.

Results

Write up your observations of this activity and relate the results to the content of this unit.

Review Questions

1. What are some of the advantages of using a file for hardness testing?
2. How does the Rockwell test differ from the Brinell test?
3. What advantage does the scleroscope tester have over the Rockwell and Brinell testers?
4. When is the Rockwell superficial hardness tester used?
5. What load, penetrator, and scale would be used for testing hardened steel on the Rockwell hardness tester?
6. What hardness numbers on the Brinell, Vickers, and Shore scleroscope would correspond to a Rockwell C 52?
7. When is spark testing necessary?
8. What determines the type of spark given off by a particular steel?
9. How may an inexperienced person fairly accurately perform a spark test?
10. Why must the grinding wheel used for spark testing be dressed clean?
11. How does the spark test of high carbon steel differ from that of low carbon steel?
12. How much pressure should be used on the grinding wheel when making a spark test?
13. What is the purpose of testing metals?
14. List six commonly used destructive testing techniques.

Films

The Art of Spark Testing, 37 min., color, Wyckoff Steel Division, Screen and Bolt Corporation of America, P.O. Box 1256, Pittsburgh, Pennsylvania 15230.

Nondestructive Testing of Metals

Objectives

AT the completion of this unit the reader (student) should be able to:

1. Name the common nondestructive testing methods.
2. Describe how each nondestructive method detects a flaw.
3. List some of the uses of nondestructive testing.
4. Inspect some metal objects by performing the experiment on liquid penetrant inspection testing.

Introduction

Trends in industry toward automation and continuous production favor nondestructive tests, since 100 percent inspection can be accomplished rapidly and economically. Developments in nondestructive testing are coming rapidly. These tests require sophisticated equipment as well as trained technicians to properly apply and evaluate them. Because the tests do not mar or destroy the material being tested, emphasis is being placed on this method.

Nondestructive Testing

Among the most commonly used nondestructive tests are radiographic, magnetic particle, liquid penetrant, ultrasonic, and eddy current tests.

Radiographic Testing

A radiograph is a picture of the inside structure of a piece of metal. Radiographic testing uses x-rays or gamma rays—high energy radiation—to locate regions of a particular material which differ in density from surrounding regions.

The procedure consists of passing radiation through the specimen to be examined and measuring the varying intensity of the radiation beam as it passes through and out of the specimen. Detection devices for the emergent beam are x-ray film, fluorescent screens, and TV x-ray systems.

Safety precautions and protection from radiation are extremely important since overexposure of these rays to the body can result in severe and permanent damage. Typical applications of radiography are found in the inspection of castings, weldings, forgings, and assemblies.

Magnetic Particle Testing

Magnetic particle tests are used for the detection of surface and subsurface flaws in ferromagnetic materials, such as iron and steel. The test is conducted by magnetizing the part to be inspected (4-18 volts). Any discontinuities in the part, such as small cracks, will produce magnetic north and south poles at opposite edges of the crack. If fine ferromagnetic particles are applied in the vicinity of the crack, these particles will be attracted to the two poles. The visible accumulation of particles will produce a readily discernible indication on the surface of the test part. Magnetic particles are available as dry powders which are dusted onto the surface to be tested and as magnetic pastes for use in oil or water suspension. Magnetic particle patterns outline the discontinuities and make them visible for inspection. Surface defects provide a tight and closely packed formation. Subsurface discontinuities have a pattern which is broad, fuzzy, and loosely packed.

Liquid Penetrant Testing

Liquid penetrant testing consists of coating the material to be tested with a liquid to test for cracks. Liquid penetrant testing includes visible dye penetrants and fluorescent penetrants, which have greater sensitivity and greater intensity of indication to fine discontinuities. Liquid penetrants can effectively be used in the inspection of nonporous metallic materials, ferrous and nonferrous. Surface discontinuities such as cracks, seams, laps, or cold shuts are indicated by this method.

The success of penetrant testing is dependent on the cleanliness of the surface being examined. It should be dry and free from rust, scale, flux, grease, paint, oil, and dirt. Because penetrant indications result from a liquid which has physically entered into a discontinuity, the parts to be inspected should be clean and dry of any cleaning agent which will hinder entrance of the penetrant.

Visible dye penetrants may be sprayed or brushed on; the dye seeks out and fills any surface cracks, discontinuities, or porosities. Fluorescent penetrant inspection makes use of a liquid that carries a dye which fluoresces brilliantly under ultraviolet light. The basic disadvantage of this method is that only surface defects can be observed.

Ultrasonic Testing

Ultrasonic testing examines parts by ultrasonic waves. The instrument used in ultrasonic flaw detection electronically generates high frequency vibrations and sends them in a pulsed beam through the part being inspected. Any discontinuity such as holes, inclusions, cracks, laminations, or seams will reflect the vibrations back to the instrument. Discontinuities are determined by the elapsed time between the initial pulse and the reflection indications shown on a cathode ray tube. High frequency ultrasonic waves tend to travel in a straight line, may be reflected by a mechanical discontinuity, and may be refracted or bent at boundaries of materials of different elastic or mechanical properties. During the test, a short pulse of ultrasonic vibrations is transmitted from a search unit into the piece being inspected. The pulsed beam travels until it meets a discontinuity; at that point it is reflected back to the receiver and displayed on the oscilloscope screen.

Inspection of thin sheets, thin-walled tubing, testing the bond between laminations of composite materials, thickness measure, and testing the metallurgical structure of metals are common applications. Ultrasonic testing is an accurate and rapid method of inspection.

Eddy Current Testing

Eddy current testing is performed by placing the specimen to be tested within the magnetic field of a coil carrying alternating electrical current. This field of alternating current induces what is known as "eddy current" within the object being tested. These eddy currents produce a magnetic field which is superimposed upon the original magnetic field. Using this method, an inspector can obtain accurate measurement of mechanical, physical, and chemical properties of a metal specimen.

Techalloy Company, Inc.

Based on the eddy current principal, this De-Tech Identifier/Comparator is used to identify unknown metals and to test wire during production.

Eddy current testing has application in sorting alloys of different composition, in control of diameter and length, in detecting cracks, porosity, shrinkage, internal stress due to cold working or corrosion attack, in evaluating heat treatment depth of surface hardening, in classifying hardness and classifying tensile strength, in measuring plating thickness of tubing, foil, sheets, and strips, and in measuring the permeability and electrical conductivity of materials.

The equipment is quite sophisticated and can measure a 1 percent variation in electrical conductivity of a piece of material. That 1 percent variation may be significant to the purchaser of the product. Eddy current nondestructive testing is extremely rapid, does not require contact with the test object, and lends itself to automatic inspection and statistical quality control.

Activities

LIQUID PENETRANT INSPECTION TEST

Problem

How is the liquid penetrant inspection test used?

Materials and Equipment

—Visible penetrant dye and developer.

—Specimen of aluminum or brass castings.

Procedure

Follow the manufacturer's suggestions; however, the general steps are:

1. Clean from the parts all rust, flux, grease, oil, film, or paint.
2. Apply a thin coating of penetrant dye.
3. Wait the prescribed penetration time suggested by the manufacturer:
   for cast aluminum, 5-15 minutes
   for brass, 10 minutes
4. Remove the penetrant by water or solvent rinse, as suggested by the manufacturer.
5. Allow the part time to dry.
6. Apply a thin coating of developer and allow it to dry. The drying time should be the same as the suggested penetration time.
7. Inspect the part:
   a crack or opening shows a red line
   a light crack shows a broken line
   porosity shows red dots
8. Clean the part after the testing is finished.

Results

Write up your observations of this activity and relate them to the content of this unit.

Review Questions

1. Define nondestructive testing of metals.
2. In what ways are radiographic testing methods used in industry?
3. Is magnetic particle testing different from radiographic testing?
4. How is liquid penetrant testing different from magnetic particle testing?
5. What is the basic shortcoming of liquid penetrant testing?
6. Differentiate between ultrasonic testing and eddy current testing.

Appendix

Hardness Tables

Relationships between values determined on Rockwell, Rockwell superficial, and Tukon hardness testers, and values determined on other testers. *

Although conversion tables dealing with hardness can only be approximate and never mathematically exact, it is of considerable value to be able to compare different hardness scales in a general way.

This table is based on the assumption that the metal tested is homogeneous to a depth several times as great at the depth of the indentation. In nonhomogeneous metal, different loads and different shapes of penetrators would penetrate—or at least meet the resistance of—metal of varying hardness, depending on the depth of the indentation. Hence, no recorded hardness value would be valid to an extent that could be confirmed by another person unless shape of penetrator and actual load applied are both specified.

The indentation hardness values measured on the various scales depend on the work hardening behavior of the material during the test; this in turn depends on the degree of previous cold working of the material. The B-scale relationships in the tables are based largely on annealed metals for the low values and cold-worked metals for the higher values. Therefore, annealed metals of high B-scale hardness, such as austenitic stainless steels, nickel, and high nickel alloys, do not conform closely to these general tables. Neither do cold-worked metals of low B-scale hardness, such as aluminum and the softer alloys. Special correlations are needed for more exact relationships in these cases.

The 15-T, 30-T, 45-T, 15-N, 30-N, and 45-N values (noted by ** in the chart heads) are in scales of the ''Rockwell'' superficial hardness tester, a specialized form of ''Rockwell'' tester, having lighter loads and a more sensitive depth reading system. It is used when, for one reason or another, the indentation must be exceptionally shallow.

Knoop Hardness Conversion. The values of the Knoop hardness number are only approximate, as they were determined on a limited number of tests and samples. These values are only for loads of 500 grams or heavier.

---

* This information and the tables on the following pages are reproduced by courtesy of Wilson Mechanical Instrument Division, American Chain & Cable Company, Inc., copyright 1952.

Hardened Steel and Hard Alloys

C 150 Kg. "Brale" — "ROCKWELL" HARDNESS TESTER	A 60 Kg. "Brale" — "ROCKWELL" HARDNESS TESTER	D 100 Kg. "Brale" — "ROCKWELL" HARDNESS TESTER	15-N 15 Kg. N "Brale" — "ROCKWELL" SUPERFICIAL HARDNESS TESTER	30-N 30 Kg. N "Brale" — "ROCKWELL" SUPERFICIAL HARDNESS TESTER	45-N 45 Kg. N "Brale" — "ROCKWELL" SUPERFICIAL HARDNESS TESTER	Diamond Pyramid Hardness 10 Kg. ◆ — SQUARE BASE DIAMOND PYRAMID - 136° Apex Angle	Knoop Hardness 500 Gr. & Over — KNOOP ELONGATED DIAMOND	Brinell Hardness 3000 Kg. ● — BRINELL HULTGREN 10mm. Ball	G 150 Kg. 1/16" Ball — "ROCKWELL" HARDNESS TESTER	Tensile Strength Approx. Only — Thousand lbs. per square inch
80	92.0	86.5	96.5	92.0	87.0	1865	—	—	—	
79	91.5	85.5	—	91.5	86.5	1787	—	—	—	
78	91.0	84.5	96.0	91.0	85.5	1710	—	—	—	
77	90.5	84.0	—	90.5	84.5	1633	—	—	—	
76	90.0	83.0	95.5	90.0	83.5	1556	—	—	—	
75	89.5	82.5	—	89.0	82.5	1478	—	—	—	INEXACT AND ONLY FOR STEEL
74	89.0	81.5	95.0	88.5	81.5	1400	—	—	—	
73	88.5	81.0	—	88.0	80.5	1323	—	—	—	
72	88.0	80.0	94.5	87.0	79.5	1245	—	—	—	
71	87.0	79.5	—	86.5	78.5	1160	—	—	—	
70	86.5	78.5	94.0	86.0	77.5	1076	972	—	—	
69	86.0	78.0	93.5	85.0	76.5	1004	946	—	—	
68	85.5	77.0	—	84.5	75.5	942	920	—	—	
67	85.0	76.0	93.0	83.5	74.5	894	895	—	—	
66	84.5	75.5	92.5	83.0	73.0	854	870	—	—	
65	84.0	74.5	92.0	82.0	72.0	820	846	—	—	
64	83.5	74.0	—	81.0	71.0	789	822	—	—	
63	83.0	73.0	91.5	80.0	70.0	763	799	—	—	
62	82.5	72.5	91.0	79.0	69.0	739	776	—	—	—
61	81.5	71.5	90.5	78.5	67.5	716	754	—	—	—
60	81.0	71.0	90.0	77.5	66.5	695	732	614	—	314
59	80.5	70.0	89.5	76.5	65.5	675	710	600	—	306
58	80.0	69.0	—	75.5	64.0	655	690	587	—	299
57	79.5	68.5	89.0	75.0	63.0	636	670	573	—	291
56	79.0	67.5	88.5	74.0	62.0	617	650	560	—	284
55	78.5	67.0	88.0	73.0	61.0	598	630	547	—	277
54	78.0	66.0	87.5	72.0	59.5	580	612	534	—	270
53	77.5	65.5	87.0	71.0	58.5	562	594	522	—	263
52	77.0	64.5	86.5	70.5	57.5	545	576	509	—	256
51	76.5	64.0	86.0	69.5	56.0	528	558	496	—	250

Hardened Steel and Hard Alloys

C 150 Kg. "Brale" "ROCKWELL" HARDNESS TESTER	A 60 Kg. "Brale" "ROCKWELL" HARDNESS TESTER	D 100 Kg. "Brale" "ROCKWELL" HARDNESS TESTER	15-N ** 15 Kg. N "Brale" "ROCKWELL" SUPERFICIAL HARDNESS TESTER	30-N ** 30 Kg. N "Brale" "ROCKWELL" SUPERFICIAL HARDNESS TESTER	45-N ** 45 Kg. N "Brale" "ROCKWELL" SUPERFICIAL HARDNESS TESTER	Diamond Pyramid Hardness 10 Kg. ◆ SQUARE BASE DIAMOND PYRAMID - 136° Apex Angle	Knoop Hardness 500 Gr. & Over ◼ KNOOP ELONGATED DIAMOND	Brinell Hardness 3000 Kg. ● BRINELL HULTGREN 10mm. Ball	G 150 Kg. 1/16" Ball "ROCKWELL" HARDNESS TESTER	Tensile Strength Approx. Only Thousand lbs. per square inch
50	76.0	63.0	85.5	68.5	55.0	513	542	484	—	243
49	75.5	62.0	85.0	67.5	54.0	498	526	472	—	236
48	74.5	61.5	84.5	66.5	52.5	485	510	460	—	230
47	74.0	60.5	84.0	66.0	51.5	471	495	448	—	223
46	73.5	60.0	83.5	65.0	50.0	458	480	437	—	217
45	73.0	59.0	83.0	64.0	49.0	446	466	426	—	211
44	72.5	58.5	82.5	63.0	48.0	435	452	415	—	205
43	72.0	57.5	82.0	62.0	46.5	424	438	404	—	199
42	71.5	57.0	81.5	61.5	45.5	413	426	393	—	194
41	71.0	56.0	81.0	60.5	44.5	403	414	382	—	188
40	70.5	55.5	80.5	59.5	43.0	393	402	372	—	182
39	70.0	54.5	80.0	58.5	42.0	383	391	362	—	177
38	69.5	54.0	79.5	57.5	41.0	373	380	352	—	171
37	69.0	53.0	79.0	56.5	39.5	363	370	342	—	166
36	68.5	52.5	78.5	56.0	38.5	353	360	332	—	162
35	68.0	51.5	78.0	55.0	37.0	343	351	322	—	157
34	67.5	50.5	77.0	54.0	36.0	334	342	313	—	153
33	67.0	50.0	76.5	53.0	35.0	325	334	305	—	148
32	66.5	49.0	76.0	52.0	33.5	317	326	297	—	144
31	66.0	48.5	75.5	51.5	32.5	309	318	290	—	140
30	65.5	47.5	75.0	50.5	31.5	301	311	283	92.0	136
29	65.0	47.0	74.5	49.5	30.0	293	304	276	91.0	132
28	64.5	46.0	74.0	48.5	29.0	285	297	270	90.0	129
27	64.0	45.5	73.5	47.5	28.0	278	290	265	89.0	126
26	63.5	44.5	72.5	47.0	26.5	271	284	260	88.0	123
25	63.0	44.0	72.0	46.0	25.5	264	278	255	87.0	120
24	62.5	43.0	71.5	45.0	24.0	257	272	250	86.0	117
23	62.0	42.5	71.0	44.0	23.0	251	266	245	84.5	115
22	61.5	41.5	70.5	43.0	22.0	246	261	240	83.5	112
21	61.0	41.0	70.0	42.5	20.5	241	256	235	82.5	110
20	60.5	40.0	69.5	41.5	19.5	236	251	230	81.0	108

Soft Steel, Grey and Malleable Cast Iron, and Most Nonferrous Metal

B 100 Kg. 1/16" Ball "ROCKWELL" HARDNESS TESTER	F 60 Kg. 1/16" Ball "ROCKWELL" HARDNESS TESTER	G 150 Kg. 1/16" Ball "ROCKWELL" HARDNESS TESTER	15-T ** 15 Kg. 1/16" Ball "ROCKWELL" SUPERFICIAL HARDNESS TESTER	30-T ** 30 Kg. 1/16" Ball "ROCKWELL" SUPERFICIAL HARDNESS TESTER	45-T ** 45 Kg. 1/16" Ball "ROCKWELL" SUPERFICIAL HARDNESS TESTER	E 100 Kg. 1/8" Ball "ROCKWELL" HARDNESS TESTER	K 150 Kg. 1/8" Ball "ROCKWELL" HARDNESS TESTER	A 60 Kg. "Brale" "ROCKWELL" HARDNESS TESTER	Knoop Hardness 500 Gr. & Over KNOOP ELONGATED DIAMOND	BRINELL Hardness 500 Kg. 10mm. Ball STANDARD BRINELL	BRINELL Hardness 3000 Kg. D.P.H. 10 Kg. SQUARE BASE DIAMOND PYRAMID 136° Apex Angle	Tensile Strength Approx. Only Thousand lbs. per square inch
100	—	82.5	93.0	82.0	72.0	—	—	61.5	251	201	240	116
99	—	81.0	92.5	81.5	71.0	—	—	61.0	246	195	234	112
98	—	79.0	—	81.0	70.0	—	—	60.0	241	189	228	109
97	—	77.5	92.0	80.5	69.0	—	—	59.5	236	184	222	106
96	—	76.0	—	80.0	68.0	—	—	59.0	231	179	216	103
95	—	74.0	91.5	79.0	67.0	—	—	58.0	226	175	210	101
94	—	72.5	—	78.5	66.0	—	—	57.5	221	171	205	98
93	—	71.0	91.0	78.0	65.5	—	—	57.0	216	167	200	96
92	—	69.0	90.5	77.5	64.5	—	100	56.5	211	163	195	93
91	—	67.5	—	77.0	63.5	—	99.5	56.0	206	160	190	91
90	—	66.0	90.0	76.0	62.5	—	98.5	55.5	201	157	185	89
89	—	64.0	89.5	75.5	61.5	—	98.0	55.0	196	154	180	87
88	—	62.5	—	75.0	60.5	—	97.0	54.0	192	151	176	85
87	—	61.0	89.0	74.5	59.5	—	96.5	53.5	188	148	172	83
86	—	59.0	88.5	74.0	58.5	—	95.5	53.0	184	145	169	81
85	—	57.5	—	73.5	58.0	—	94.5	52.5	180	142	165	80
84	—	56.0	88.0	73.0	57.0	—	94.0	52.0	176	140	162	78
83	—	54.0	87.5	72.0	56.0	—	93.0	51.0	173	137	159	77
82	—	52.5	—	71.5	55.0	—	92.0	50.5	170	135	156	75
81	—	51.0	87.0	71.0	54.0	—	91.0	50.0	167	133	153	74
80	—	49.0	86.5	70.0	53.0	—	90.5	49.5	164	130	150	72

Soft Steel, Grey and Malleable Cast Iron, and Most Nonferrous Metal

B 100 Kg. 1/16" Ball "ROCKWELL" HARDNESS TESTER	F 60 Kg. 1/16" Ball "ROCKWELL" HARDNESS TESTER	G 150 Kg. 1/16" Ball "ROCKWELL" HARDNESS TESTER	15-T 15 Kg. 1/16" Ball "ROCKWELL" SUPERFICIAL HARDNESS TESTER	30-T 30 Kg. 1/16" Ball "ROCKWELL" SUPERFICIAL HARDNESS TESTER	45-T 45 Kg. 1/16" Ball "ROCKWELL" SUPERFICIAL HARDNESS TESTER	E 100 Kg. 1/8" Ball "ROCKWELL" HARDNESS TESTER	K 150 Kg. 1/8" Ball "ROCKWELL" HARDNESS TESTER	A 60 Kg. "Brale" "ROCKWELL" HARDNESS TESTER	Knoop Hardness 500 Gr. & Over KNOOP ELONGATED DIAMOND	BRINELL Hardness 500 Kg. 10mm. Ball STANDARD BRINELL	BRINELL 3000 Kg. D.P.H. 10 Kg. SQUARE BASE DIAMOND PYRAMID-136° Apex Angle	Tensile Strength Approx. Only Thousand lbs. per square inch
79	—	47.5	—	69.5	52.0	—	89.5	49.0	161	128	147	
78	—	46.0	86.0	69.0	51.0	—	88.5	48.5	158	126	144	
77	—	44.0	85.5	68.0	50.0	—	88.0	48.0	155	124	141	
76	—	42.5	—	67.5	49.0	—	87.0	47.0	152	122	139	
75	99.5	41.0	85.0	67.0	48.5	—	86.0	46.5	150	120	137	
74	99.0	39.0	—	66.0	47.5	—	85.0	46.0	147	118	135	
73	98.5	37.5	84.5	65.5	46.5	—	84.5	45.5	145	116	132	
72	98.0	36.0	84.0	65.0	45.5	—	83.5	45.0	143	114	130	
71	97.5	34.5	—	64.0	44.5	100	82.5	44.5	141	112	127	
70	97.0	32.5	83.5	63.5	43.5	99.5	81.5	44.0	139	110	125	
69	96.0	31.0	83.0	62.5	42.5	99.0	81.0	43.5	137	109	123	
68	95.5	29.5	—	62.0	41.5	98.0	80.0	43.0	135	107	121	
67	95.0	28.0	82.5	61.5	40.5	97.5	79.0	42.5	133	106	119	
66	94.5	26.5	82.0	60.5	39.5	97.0	78.0	42.0	131	104	117	
65	94.0	25.0	—	60.0	38.5	96.0	77.5	—	129	102	116	
64	93.5	23.5	81.5	59.5	37.5	95.5	76.5	41.5	127	101	114	
63	93.0	22.0	81.0	58.5	36.5	95.0	75.5	41.0	125	99	112	
62	92.0	20.5	—	58.0	35.5	94.5	74.5	40.5	124	98	110	
61	91.5	19.0	80.5	57.0	34.5	93.5	74.0	40.0	122	96	108	
60	91.0	17.5	—	56.5	33.5	93.0	73.0	39.5	120	95	107	
59	90.5	16.0	80.0	56.0	32.0	92.5	72.0	39.0	118	94	106	
58	90.0	14.5	79.5	55.0	31.0	92.0	71.0	38.5	117	92	104	
57	89.5	13.0	—	54.5	30.0	91.0	70.5	38.0	115	91	103	
56	89.0	11.5	79.0	54.0	29.0	90.5	69.5	—	114	90	101	
55	88.0	10.0	78.5	53.0	28.0	90.0	68.5	37.5	112	89	100	
54	87.5	8.5	—	52.5	27.0	89.5	68.0	37.0	111	87	—	
53	87.0	7.0	78.0	51.5	26.0	89.0	67.0	36.5	110	86	—	
52	86.5	5.5	77.5	51.0	25.0	88.0	66.0	36.0	109	85	—	
51	86.0	4.0	—	50.5	24.0	87.5	65.0	35.5	108	84	—	
50	85.5	2.5	77.0	49.5	23.0	87.0	64.5	35.0	107	83	—	

Even for steel, Tensile Strength relation to hardness is inexact, unless determined for specific material.

Soft Steel, Grey and Malleable Cast Iron, and Most Nonferrous Metal

B 100 Kg 1/16" Ball "ROCKWELL" HARDNESS TESTER	F 60 Kg. 1/16" Ball "ROCKWELL" HARDNESS TESTER	15-T •• 15 Kg. 1/16" Ball "ROCKWELL" SUPERFICIAL HARDNESS TESTER	30-T •• 30 Kg. 1/16" Ball "ROCKWELL" SUPERFICIAL HARDNESS TESTER	45-T •• 45 Kg. 1/16" Ball "ROCKWELL" SUPERFICIAL HARDNESS TESTER	E 100 Kg. 1/8" Ball "ROCKWELL" HARDNESS TESTER	H 60 Kg. 1/8" Ball "ROCKWELL" HARDNESS TESTER	K 150 Kg. 1/8" Ball "ROCKWELL" HARDNESS TESTER	A 60 Kg. "Brale" "ROCKWELL" HARDNESS TESTER	Knoop Hardness 500 Gr. & Over KNOOP ELONGATED DIAMOND	Brinell Hardness 500 Kg. 10mm. Ball STANDARD BRINELL
50	85.5	77.0	49.5	23.0	87.0	—	64.5	35.0	107	83
49	85.0	76.5	49.0	22.0	86.5	—	63.5	—	106	82
48	84.5	—	48.5	20.5	85.5	—	62.5	34.5	105	81
47	84.0	76.0	47.5	19.5	85.0	—	61.5	34.0	104	80
46	83.0	75.5	47.0	18.5	84.5	—	61.0	33.5	103	—
45	82.5	—	46.0	17.5	84.0	—	60.0	33.0	102	79
44	82.0	75.0	45.5	16.5	83.5	—	59.0	32.5	101	78
43	81.5	74.5	45.0	15.5	82.5	—	58.0	32.0	100	77
42	81.0	—	44.0	14.5	82.0	—	57.5	31.5	99	76
41	80.5	74.0	43.5	13.5	81.5	—	56.5	31.0	98	75
40	79.5	73.5	43.0	12.5	81.0	—	55.5	—	97	—
39	79.0	—	42.0	11.0	80.0	—	54.5	30.5	96	74
38	78.5	73.0	41.5	10.0	79.5	—	54.0	30.0	95	73
37	78.0	72.5	40.5	9.0	79.0	—	53.0	29.5	94	72
36	77.5	—	40.0	8.0	78.5	100	52.0	29.0	93	—
35	77.0	72.0	39.5	7.0	78.0	99.5	51.5	28.5	92	71
34	76.5	71.5	38.5	6.0	77.0	99.0	50.5	28.0	91	70
33	75.5	—	38.0	5.0	76.5	—	49.5	—	90	69
32	75.0	71.0	37.5	4.0	76.0	98.5	48.5	27.5	89	—
31	74.5	—	36.5	3.0	75.5	98.0	48.0	27.0	88	68
30	74.0	70.5	36.0	2.0	75.0	—	47.0	26.5	—	67
29	73.5	70.0	35.5	1.0	74.0	97.5	46.0	26.0	—	—
28	73.0	—	34.5	—	73.5	97.0	45.0	25.5	—	66
27	72.5	69.5	34.0	—	73.0	96.5	44.5	25.0	85	—

Soft Steel, Grey and Malleable Cast Iron, and Most Nonferrous Metal

B 100 kg 1/16" Ball "ROCKWELL" HARDNESS TESTER	F 60 Kg. 1/16" Ball "ROCKWELL" HARDNESS TESTER	15-T ** 15 Kg. 1/16" Ball "ROCKWELL" SUPERFICIAL HARDNESS TESTER	30-T ** 30 Kg. 1/16" Ball "ROCKWELL" SUPERFICIAL HARDNESS TESTER	45-T ** 45 Kg. 1/16" Ball "ROCKWELL" SUPERFICIAL HARDNESS TESTER	E 100 Kg. 1/8" Ball "ROCKWELL" HARDNESS TESTER	H 60 Kg. 1/8" Ball "ROCKWELL" HARDNESS TESTER	K 150 Kg. 1/8" Ball "ROCKWELL" HARDNESS TESTER	A 60 Kg. "Brale" "ROCKWELL" HARDNESS TESTER	Knoop Hardness 500 Gr. & Over KNOOP ELONGATED DIAMOND	Brinell Hardness 500 Kg. 10mm. Ball STANDARD BRINELL
26	72.0	69.0	33.0	—	72.5	—	43.5	24.5	—	65
25	71.0	—	32.5	—	72.0	96.0	42.5	—	—	64
24	70.5	68.5	32.0	—	71.0	95.5	41.5	24.0	—	—
23	70.0	68.0	31.0	—	70.5	—	41.0	23.5	82	63
22	69.5	—	30.5	—	70.0	95.0	40.0	23.0	—	—
21	69.0	67.5	29.5	—	69.5	94.5	39.0	22.5	—	62
20	68.5	—	29.0	—	68.5	—	38.0	22.0	—	—
19	68.0	67.0	28.5	—	68.0	94.0	37.5	21.5	79	61
18	67.0	66.5	27.5	—	67.5	93.5	36.5	—	—	—
17	66.5	—	27.0	—	67.0	93.0	35.5	21.0	—	60
16	66.0	66.0	26.0	—	66.5	—	35.0	20.5	—	—
15	65.5	65.5	25.5	—	65.5	92.5	34.0	20.0	76	59
14	65.0	—	25.0	—	65.0	92.0	33.0	—	—	—
13	64.5	65.0	24.0	—	64.5	—	32.0	—	—	58
12	64.0	64.5	23.5	—	64.0	91.5	31.5	—	—	—
11	63.5	—	23.0	—	63.5	91.0	30.5	—	73	—
10	63.0	64.0	22.0	—	62.5	90.5	29.5	—	—	57
9	62.0	—	21.5	—	62.0	—	29.0	—	—	—
8	61.5	63.5	20.5	—	61.5	90.0	28.0	—	71	—
7	61.0	63.0	20.0	—	61.0	89.5	27.0	—	—	56
6	60.5	—	19.5	—	60.5	—	26.0	—	—	—
5	60.0	62.5	18.5	—	60.0	89.0	25.5	—	69	55
4	59.5	62.0	18.0	—	59.0	88.5	24.5	—	—	—
3	59.0	—	17.0	—	58.5	88.0	23.5	—	—	—
2	58.0	61.5	16.5	—	58.0	—	23.0	—	68	54
1	57.5	61.0	16.0	—	57.5	87.5	22.0	—	—	—
0	57.0	—	15.0	—	57.0	87.0	21.0	—	67	53

References

Allen, Dell K. *Metallurgy Theory and Practice*. Chicago: American Technical Society, 1969.

American Iron and Steel Institute. *Steelmaking Flow Charts*. Washington, D.C.: American Iron and Steel Institute, Public Relations Department, 1964.

———. *The Making of Steel*. Washington, D.C.: American Iron and Steel Institute, 1964.

American Society for Metals. *Metals Handbook*. Metals Park, Ohio: American Society for Metals, 1961 (vol. 1), 1964 (vol. 2).

Giachino, J.W., and Schoenhals, Neil L. *General Metals for Technology*. Milwaukee, Wisconsin: Bruce Publishing Co., 1964.

Johnson, Harold V. *Technical Metals*. Peoria, Illinois: Chas. A. Bennett Co., 1968.

Kazanas, H.C., Klein, Roy S., and Lindbeck, John R. *Technology of Industrial Materials*. Peoria, Illinois: Chas. A. Bennett Co., 1974.

Kazanas, H.C., and Wallace, D.F. *Materials Testing Laboratory Manual*. Peoria, Illinois: Chas. A. Bennett Co., 1974.

Ludwig, O.J., McCarthy, W.J., and Repp, V.E. *Metal Work Technology and Practice*. Bloomington, Illinois: McKnight and McKnight Publishing Co., 1962.

Mantell, C.L., ed. *Engineering Materials Handbook*. New York: McGraw-Hill Book Co., 1958.

Materials. A Scientific American Book. San Francisco: W.H. Freeman and Co., 1967.

Miller, Rex, and Morrison, Thomas J. *Metal Technology*. Indianapolis, Indiana: Howard W. Sams and Co., 1975.

Patton, W.J. *Materials in Industry*. Englewood Cliffs, New Jersey: Prentice-Hall, 1976.

Pollack, H.W. *Materials Science and Metallurgy*. Reston, Virginia: Reston Publishing Co., 1973.

Ross, Robert M. *Metallic Materials Specification Handbook*. New York: Halsted Press, A Division of John Wiley and Sons, 1972.

United States Steel Corp. *Laboratory Experiments in the Chemistry and Physics of Steel*. Pittsburgh, Pennsylvania: United States Steel Corp., 1962.

―――. *Suiting the Heat Treatment to the Job: A Review of Metallurgical Principles for Heat Treatment of Steels*. Pittsburgh, Pennsylvania: United States Steel Corp., 1968.

Index